SIDE by SIDE Interactive

WITHDRAWN

ACTIVITY WORKBOOK

2B

A self-study companion to
Side by Side Interactive **multimedia software**
and
Side by Side TV **videos**

Steven J. Molinsky

Bill Bliss

Contributing Authors
Dorothy Lynde
Susanna Minton

Longman

longman.com

ACTIVITY WORKBOOK 2B

Side by Side Interactive Activity Workbook 2B
Copyright © 2004 by Prentice Hall Regents
Addison Wesley Longman, Inc.
A Pearson Education Company.

Pearson Education, 10 Bank Street, White Plains, NY 10606

Editorial manager: *Pam Fishman*
Vice president, director of design and production: *Rhea Banker*
Director of electronic production: *Aliza Greenblatt*
Production manager: *Ray Keating*
Director of manufacturing: *Patrice Fraccio*
Associate digital layout manager: *Paula D. Williams*
Cover design: *Monika Popowitz*

Project manager: *Harriet Dishman*
Design and composition: *PC&F, Inc.*
Video stills: *Elizabeth Gallagher*
Illustrator: *Richard E. Hill*

The authors gratefully acknowledge the contribution
of Tina Carver in the development of the original
Side by Side program.

ISBN 0-13-110764-X

3 4 5 6 7 8 9 10 – WC – 06 05

CONTENTS

• • • • • • PREFACE • • • • • •

The **Side by Side Interactive** Activity Workbooks are designed to serve as self-study companions to the **Side by Side Interactive** multimedia software program and the **Side by Side TV** videos. The Activity Workbooks supplement the technology-based language instruction through motivating activities that are individualized, self-paced, easy-to-use, and fun!

This volume, Activity Workbook 2B, provides up to 60 hours of supplemental practice for Level 2B (Segments 40-52) of the program. It can be used at home, in school, or in any other setting. (The total program contains 52 segments. Learners who complete one segment each week can therefore complete the program in one year.)

FEATURES OF THE ACTIVITY WORKBOOK

- SEGMENT OPENING PAGES indicate the language focus and key vocabulary in the segment and describe the scenes, songs, and other video-based lessons contained in the multimedia software program and in the videos.

- EXERCISES and ACTIVITIES help learners interact with the video-based lessons in each segment. Certain exercises and activities require use of the video material and are indicated with the symbol 🔑📼. Learners can choose to do these exercises and activities before, during, or after they watch the video material.

- SCRIPTS are provided at the end of each workbook segment. Learners can read along as they watch, read before to preview the material, or read later for review and practice.

- A SUMMARY PAGE provides grammar charts and highlights functional expressions featured in each segment.

- An ANSWER KEY enables learners to check their work.

The mission of *Side by Side Interactive* and *Side by Side TV* is to offer learners of English exciting, motivating, and effective language instruction through multimedia software and video. We hope that this companion Activity Workbook helps to provide a language-learning experience that is dynamic, interactive, . . . and fun!

Steven J. Molinsky
Bill Bliss

HOW TO READ LESSON HEADINGS:

Side by Side Interactive
Segment & Lesson Number

↓

1.1 WHAT'S YOUR NAME?   (:09)◄──   *Side by Side TV* Video Clock Time

↑
Lesson Title

To find the video material for lessons in this workbook:
Side by Side Interactive multimedia software users should use the Segment & Lesson Numbers.
Side by Side TV video users should use the Video Clock Times.

🔑📼 indicates a workbook activity that requires the user to view the corresponding video material—either in the multimedia software program or in the videos.

v

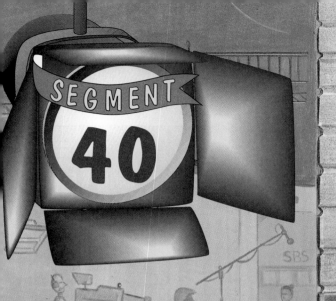

40

- **Directions**
- **Getting Around Town**
- **Public Transportation**

"Take the subway and the bus. Would you like to come with us? . . . Traveling Side by Side."

LESSON MENU

SBS-TV Backstage Bulletin Board

TO: Production Crew
Sets and props for this segment:

Outdoors
bench
bus stop sign
subway sign

Bus terminal
counter
information sign

TO: Cast Members
Key words in this segment:

barber shop
church
hotel
pet shop

subway
bus

avenue
boulevard

take the bus
take the subway
get off (at)
walk up
walk down

on the right
on the left
at the corner (of)

40.1 WHAT'S THE QUICKEST WAY TO GET THERE? (:10)

DIRECTION CHECK

Circle the correct places.

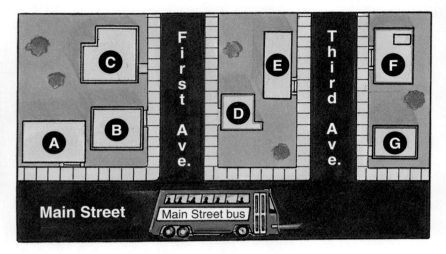

1 Where is Peter's Pet Shop? **A B C D E F G**

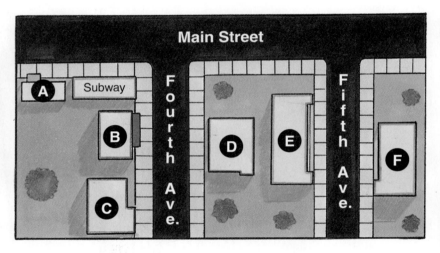

2 Where is Harry's Barber Shop? **A B C D E F**

EDITING MIX-UP

The video editor made a mistake! Put the following lines in the correct order.

_____ Thank you very much.

_____ Take the subway and get off at Fourth Avenue.

_____ You're welcome.

__1__ Excuse me. What's the easiest way to get to Harry's Barber Shop?

_____ Walk down Fourth Avenue and you'll see Harry's Barber Shop on the left.

_____ Take _____¹ the Main Street bus and _____² at

_____³ Avenue. _____⁴ Second Avenue and you'll see

Christy's Cafeteria _____⁵.

_____⁶ the subway and _____⁷ at First Avenue.

_____⁸ First Avenue and you'll see Bob's Bowling Lanes

_____⁹.

_____¹⁰ the subway and _____¹¹ at Fourth Avenue.

_____¹² Fourth Avenue and you'll see Lindy's Laundromat

_____¹³.

40.2 CAN YOU TELL ME HOW TO GET THERE? (:53)

YES OR NO?

1. The tourist asks the person in the information booth to recommend a good hotel.   (Yes)   No

2. She recommends the Bearview Hotel.   Yes   No

3. She thinks it's a good hotel.   Yes   No

4. She knows how to get there.   Yes   No

5. She says to take the bus and get off at Brighton Boulevard.   Yes   No

6. The hotel is at the corner of Brighton Boulevard and Twelfth Street.   Yes   No

ON CAMERA

You're a tourist-information person! Answer these people's questions about your town.

1. Can you recommend a good restaurant?

....
....
....

2. Can you recommend a good gift shop?

....
....
....

3. Can you recommend an interesting museum?

....
....
....

4. Can you recommend a good place to listen to music ?

....
....
....

40.3 HOW DO I GET TO ST. ANDREW'S CHURCH? (1:20)

Give these people directions to St. Andrew's Church.

___Take the subway___ ¹ and _____ ² at _____ ³ Avenue.

_____ ⁴ _____ ⁵ Avenue and you'll see the church

_____ ⁶ .

FUNCTION CHECK

1. "Excuse me." (a.) attracting attention   b. asking for directions

2. "What's the best way to get to St. Andrew's Church?"   a. asking for directions   b. giving directions

3. "Thank you very much."   a. attracting attention   b. expressing gratitude

4. "Take the subway and get off at Seventh Avenue."   a. giving directions   b. asking directions

5. "Did you say Second Avenue?"   a. asking directions   b. checking understanding

6. "No. Seventh Avenue."   a. giving directions   b. correcting

7. "When you get off, walk down Seventh Avenue and you'll see the church on the right."   a. giving directions   b. expressing gratitude

DID YOU NOTICE?

___c___ 1. Three of these people are going to a _____.   a. wedding gown

_____ 2. The bride is wearing a white _____.   b. his money

_____ 3. The groom is wearing a black _____.   c. wedding

_____ 4. The last person to ask for directions is a _____.   d. clergyman

_____ 5. The young man on the street is counting _____.   e. tuxedo

GETTING AROUND SUNNYVILLE

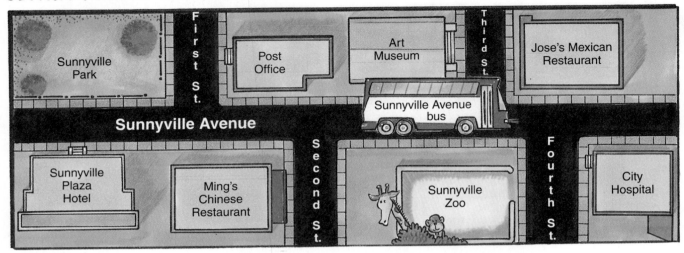

Carol Peterson is a tourist in Sunnyville. Look at the map and answer her questions.

I'm at the Sunnyville Plaza Hotel. What's the easiest way to get to the Art Museum?

_____Take_____ ¹ the Sunnyville Avenue bus and _____ ² at Third Street. _____ ³ Third Street and you'll see the Art Museum _____ ⁴.

I'm on Sunnyville Avenue. What's the most direct way to get to the Sunnyville Zoo?

_____ ⁵ the Sunnyville Avenue bus and _____ ⁶ at Fourth Street. _____ ⁷ Fourth Street and you'll see the Sunnyville Zoo _____ ⁸.

I'm at the Sunnyville Zoo. What's the best way to get to the Sunnyville Park?

_____ ⁹ the Sunnyville Avenue bus and _____ ¹⁰ at _____ ¹¹. _____ ¹².

I'm at the City Hospital. What's the quickest way to Ming's Chinese Restaurant?

....
....

40.1 WHAT'S THE QUICKEST WAY TO GET THERE? (:10)

PERSON 1: Excuse me. What's the quickest way to get to Peter's Pet Shop?

PERSON 2: Take the Main Street bus and get off at First Avenue. Walk up First Avenue and you'll see Peter's Pet Shop on the right.

PERSON 1: Thank you very much.

PERSON 2: You're welcome.

PERSON 3: Excuse me. What's the easiest way to get to Harry's Barber Shop?

PERSON 4: Take the subway and get off at Fourth Avenue. Walk down Fourth Avenue and you'll see Harry's Barber Shop on the left.

PERSON 3: Thank you very much.

PERSON 4: You're welcome.

40.2 CAN YOU TELL ME HOW TO GET THERE? (:53)

TRAVELER: Can you recommend a good hotel?

ATTENDANT: Yes. The Bellview is a good hotel. I think it's one of the best hotels in town.

TRAVELER: Can you tell me how to get there?

ATTENDANT: Sure. Take the subway and get off at Brighton Boulevard. You'll see the Bellview at the corner of Brighton Boulevard and Twelfth Street.

TRAVELER: Thank you very much.

ATTENDANT: You're welcome.

40.3 HOW DO I GET TO ST. ANDREW'S CHURCH? (1:20)

BRIDE: Excuse me. What's the best way to get to St. Andrew's Church?

YOUNG MAN: St. Andrew's Church? Hmm. Take the subway and get off at Seventh Avenue. Walk down Seventh Avenue and you'll see the church on your right.

BRIDE: Thank you very much.

YOUNG MAN: You're welcome.

GROOM: Excuse me. What's the most direct way to get to St. Andrew's Church?

YOUNG MAN: It's very easy. Take the subway and get off at Seventh Avenue.

GROOM: Did you say Second Avenue?

YOUNG MAN: No. Seventh Avenue. When you get off, walk down Seventh Avenue and you'll see the church on the right.

GROOM: Thanks.

YOUNG MAN: Don't mention it.

PRIEST: Excuse me. I'm really in a hurry.

YOUNG MAN: Don't tell me! You're going to St. Andrew's Church.

PRIEST: That's right! How did you know?

YOUNG MAN: Oh, I just guessed. Take the subway and get off at Seventh Avenue. Walk down Seventh Avenue and you'll see the church on your right.

PRIEST: Thank you so much.

YOUNG MAN: You're welcome.

GRAMMAR

Imperatives

> **Take** the subway.
> **Get off** at First Avenue.
> **Walk** down Fourth Avenue.

FUNCTIONS

Asking for Directions

What's the quickest/easiest/best/
  most direct way to get to *Peter's
  Pet Shop?*

Can you tell me how to get there?

Giving Directions

Take *the Main Street bus* and get
  off at *First Avenue.*

Take *the subway* and get off at
  Seventh Avenue.

Walk up *First Avenue.*
Walk down *First Avenue.*

You'll see *the church* on the right/
  on your right.
You'll see *the church* on the left/
  on your left.

You'll see *the hotel* at the corner
  of *Brighton Boulevard* and
  Twelfth Street.

Attracting Attention

Excuse me.

Expressing Gratitude

Thanks.
Thank you very much.
Thank you so much.

Responding to Gratitude

You're welcome.
Don't mention it!

Asking for a Suggestion

Can you recommend *a good
  hotel?*

Describing

The Bellview is a good *hotel.*

I think it's one of the best *hotels*
  in *town.*

Checking Understanding

Did you say *Second Avenue?*

SEGMENT 41

- Comparative of Adverbs
- Agent Nouns
- Describing People's Actions

"He's driving very carelessly. He should drive more carefully . . . Side by Side."

LESSON MENU

SBS-TV Backstage Bulletin Board

TO: Production Crew
Sets and props for this segment:

Taxi

Living Room
  lamp
  television
  remote control
  table
  chairs

Office
  typewriters
  desks
  file cabinets
  telephone

Stage
  hats
  canes

TO: Cast Members
Key words in this segment:

accurate	late	actor
beautiful	loud	chess player
careful	magnificent	dancer
careless	neat	driver
early	polite	painter
fast	quick	reporter
good	sloppy	singer
graceful	slow	
impolite	soft	

41.1 HE DRIVES VERY CARELESSLY (2:45)

YES OR NO?

1	The passengers think the driver is careful.	Yes	(No)
2	They think the driver is careless.	Yes	No
3	They think he drives carefully.	Yes	No
4	They think he drives carelessly.	Yes	No
5	The driver is driving slowly.	Yes	No
6	The passengers are pleased.	Yes	No
7	The passengers are angry.	Yes	No
8	The driver is pleasant.	Yes	No

WHAT DO YOU THINK?

What do you think the taxi driver is thinking?

WHAT'S THE LINE?

1 He's a very _____ typist.

　(a.) quick

　b. quickly

2 John speaks very _____.

　a. soft

　b. softly

3 They're very _____ dressers.

　a. sloppy

　b. sloppily

4 Kevin works very _____.

　a. careless

　b. carelessly

5 Jill speaks very _____ to her parents.

　a. impolite

　b. impolitely

6 We arrived at the party very

　_____.

　a. late

　b. lately

10

41.2 REMOTE CONTROL (3:03)

SOUND CHECK

1. She's a (beautiful   beautifully) singer.

   She sings very (beautiful   beautifully).

2. He's a (good   well) actor.

   He acts very (good   well).

3. He's a (magnificent   magnificently) painter.

   He paints (magnificent   magnificently).

4. She's a very (graceful   gracefully) dancer.

   She dances very (graceful   gracefully).

5. He's a (fast   fastly) driver!

   He drives very (fast   fastly).

6. He's a very (accurate   accurately) reporter.

   He reports very (accurate   accurately).

7. He's a (slow   slowly) chess player.

   He plays chess very (slow   slowly).

Circle the correct response.

1 She's a beautiful singer.

   a. You're right.

   b. You right.

2 He's a good actor.

   a. I'm agree.

   b. I agree.

3 What is this? PBS?

   a. I think to.

   b. I think so.

4 He's a magnificent painter.

   a. He is.

   b. He sure does.

5 Boy! He's a fast driver!

   a. He sure is.

   b. He sure does.

6 He's a slow chess player.

   a. I say!

   b. I'll say!

SCRAMBLED SOUND TRACK

The sound track is all mixed up. Put the words in the correct order.

HUSBAND: | that's | I | tonight. | enough | think | TV | Well, | for |

_____

_____

WIFE: | well! | night, | Sleep | Good | dear. |

_____

RATE YOURSELF

How do you do the following things? Do you do them carefully/beautifully/carelessly/well/gracefully/. . . ? You decide.

I sing ....

I act ....

I dance ....

I drive ....

I speak ....

I work ....

I type ....

I play the ....
                  (musical instrument)

I play ....
              (sport)

41.3 OFFICE TALK (5:55)

OPPOSITES

Help the actors prepare their lines.

__d__ **1** I don't work quickly. I work _____.

_____ **2** Don't sing loudly. Sing _____.

_____ **3** He doesn't write neatly. He writes _____.

_____ **4** You shouldn't come to class late. You should come _____.

_____ **5** I don't ski carelessly anymore. I ski _____.

_____ **6** Don't speak to your teacher impolitely. Speak _____.

a. softly

b. sloppily

c. carefully

d. slowly

e. politely

f. early

SOUND CHECK

1 Bob speaks very

_____quickly_____.

He should try to
speak more

_____slowly_____.

2 Francine speaks very

_____.

She should try to speak

_____.

3 George dresses very

_____.

He should try to
dress more

_____.

4 Every day Edith
comes to work

_____.

She should come
to work

_____.

5 Dennis talks to
the boss very

_____.

He should try to speak
to Mr. Jenkins more

_____.

6 Sally and Mark don't
usually type so

_____.

They should type more

_____ in
the future.

YES OR NO?

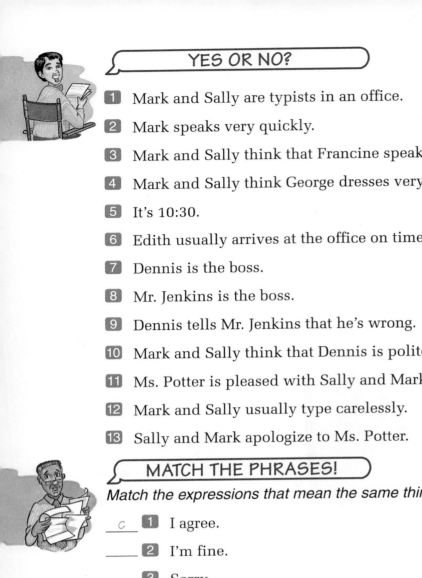

1	Mark and Sally are typists in an office.	(Yes)	No
2	Mark speaks very quickly.	Yes	No
3	Mark and Sally think that Francine speaks very loudly.	Yes	No
4	Mark and Sally think George dresses very sloppily.	Yes	No
5	It's 10:30.	Yes	No
6	Edith usually arrives at the office on time.	Yes	No
7	Dennis is the boss.	Yes	No
8	Mr. Jenkins is the boss.	Yes	No
9	Dennis tells Mr. Jenkins that he's wrong.	Yes	No
10	Mark and Sally think that Dennis is polite.	Yes	No
11	Ms. Potter is pleased with Sally and Mark's typing.	Yes	No
12	Mark and Sally usually type carelessly.	Yes	No
13	Sally and Mark apologize to Ms. Potter.	Yes	No

MATCH THE PHRASES!

Match the expressions that mean the same thing.

__c__ **1** I agree.   a. Everything's great!

_____ **2** I'm fine.   b. How are you doing today?

_____ **3** Sorry.   c. I'll say!

_____ **4** How are you today?   d. I apologize.

HOW ABOUT YOU?

What are some things you do, and how do you do them?

1 quickly / slowly

....

....

2 softly / loudly

....

....

3 sloppily / neatly

....

....

4 late / early

....

....

5 impolitely / politely

....

....

6 carelessly / carefully

....

....

41.4 TRY A LITTLE HARDER (8:36)

Let's say you're a driver,

A careful/carefully [1] driver who

Drives very careful/carefully [2] ,

As careful/carefully [3] drivers do.

Just try a little harder.

You can find a way.

Try to drive more careful/carefully [4] today.

Let's say you're a singer,

A beautiful/beautifully [5] singer who

Sings very beautiful/beautifully [6] ,

As beautiful/beautifully [7] singers do.

Just try a little harder.

You can find a way.

Try to sing more beautiful/beautifully [8] today.

Let's say you're a dancer,

A graceful/gracefully [9] dancer who

Dances very graceful/gracefully [10] ,

As graceful/gracefully [11] dancers do.

Just try a little harder.

You can find a way.

Try to dance more graceful/gracefully [12] today.

Just try a little harder.

That's what we always say.

Sing a little strong/stronger [13] .

Work a little long/longer [14] .

Do a little good/better [15] every day.

Do a little good/better [16] every day.

WRITE YOUR OWN LAST VERSE!

Let's say you're a ....,

A .... who

.... very .... ,

As .... do.

Just try a little harder.

You can find a way.

Try to .... more .... today.

THE PEOPLE IN GARY'S OFFICE

 Gary is a hard worker. But he thinks some of his co-workers don't work as hard as he does. Finish Gary's thoughts below.

1 Karen / speak to her co-workers / unprofessional

Karen speaks to her co-workers

unprofessionally. She should speak

to them more professionally.

2 Mike / answer the telephone / impolite

_____

_____

_____

3 Ray / write reports / incorrect

_____

_____

_____

4 the bookkeeper / keep the books / inaccurate

_____

_____

_____

5 Amy / make presentations / ineffective

_____

_____

_____

6 the president / run the company / inefficient

_____

_____

_____

A LETTER TO A FRIEND

Pam recently moved from Greenville to Sunnyville. Help her finish her letter to a friend in Greenville, using the correct form of the adjective or adverb.

Dear Laurie,

Life here in Sunnyville is very _____exciting_____ [1]. There are a lot
(exciting)

of enjoyable things to do. Last night I went to a band concert downtown. The band

played very _____ [2]. Actually, I think the band here plays
(good)

even _____ [3] than the band in Greenville. There is also
(good)

a large lake here. I love to walk _____ [4] around the lake
(slow)

on a hot summer day. By the way, the food here is _____ [5]. I
(excellent)

found some _____ [6] restaurants to eat in. Actually, I think
(inexpensive)

I can eat much more _____ [7] and _____ [8]
(cheap)   (nutritious)

here in Sunnyville than in Greenville.

Let me tell you about the people. Everybody here is very _____ [9].
(friendly)

People don't speak as _____ [10] as the people in Greenville.
(quick)

They're much _____ [11] and more _____ [12].
(nice)   (polite)

Even the taxi drivers here are _____ [13]. They drive very
(pleasant)

_____ [14] and _____ [15]. I'm so
(careful)   (courteous)

_____ [16] that I'm living here! I hope you can visit soon.
(pleased)

Pam

SEGMENT 41 SCRIPT ●●●●●●●●●●●●●●●●●●●●●●●●

41.1 HE DRIVES VERY CARELESSLY

(2:45)

PASSENGER 1: I think he's a careless driver.
PASSENGER 2: I agree. He drives VERY carelessly.

41.2 REMOTE CONTROL (3:03)

HUSBAND: She's a beautiful singer.
WIFE: You're right. She sings very beautifully.

WIFE: He's a good actor.
HUSBAND: I agree. He acts very well.

HUSBAND: What is this? PBS?
WIFE: I think so.
HUSBAND: He's a magnificent painter.
WIFE: He is. He paints magnificently.

WIFE: Look at her! She's a very graceful dancer.
HUSBAND: You're right. She dances very gracefully.

HUSBAND: Boy! He's a fast driver!
WIFE: He sure is. He drives very fast.

WIFE: He's a very accurate reporter.

HUSBAND: I agree. He reports very accurately.

HUSBAND: He's a slow chess player.
WIFE: I'll say! He plays chess very slowly.

HUSBAND: Well, I think that's enough TV for tonight.
WIFE: Good night, dear. Sleep well!

(The wife turns the TV back on and sings.)

"We are the world. We are the children."

41.3 OFFICE TALK (5:55)

BOB: Hi, Mark. Hi, Sally. How are you today? Sorry I can't talk right now. I'm very busy. Hope you have a nice day. See you later. Bye.
MARK: Bob speaks very quickly.
SALLY: You're right. He should try to speak more slowly.

FRANCINE: Hello, Mark. Hi, Sally. How are you doing today?
MARK: I'm fine, Francine.
SALLY: Everything's great, Francine.
FRANCINE: That's good. Have a nice day.
SALLY: You know . . . Francine speaks very softly.
MARK: You're right. She should try to speak louder.

MARK: I think George dresses very sloppily.

SALLY: I agree with you. He should try to dress more neatly.

EDITH: Hi, Sally. Hi, Mark. Oh, my! Is it 9:30 already? I guess my watch is broken again. Well, good-bye. Have a nice day.

SALLY: Have a nice day, Edith.

MARK: See you later, Edith. You know . . . I just don't understand Edith. Every day she comes to work late.

SALLY: I know. She should come to work earlier.

MARK: Hmm.

DENNIS: I don't agree with you, Mr. Jenkins. I just don't agree with you. It's a bad idea.

MR. JENKINS: Why do you say that, Dennis?

DENNIS: I just know I'm right. You can't always be right, Mr. Jenkins. And this time, you're wrong!

SALLY: Dennis talks to the boss very impolitely.

MARK: You're absolutely right. He should try to speak to Mr. Jenkins more politely.

MS. POTTER: Mark? Sally?

MARK: Yes, Ms. Potter?

MS. POTTER: Who typed these letters?

SALLY: I typed that one, Ms. Potter.

MARK: And that one is mine.

MS. POTTER: Look at all the mistakes! I'm very disappointed. You don't usually type so carelessly.

SALLY: Sorry, Ms. Potter.

MARK: I apologize, Ms. Potter.

MS. POTTER: Please try to type more carefully in the future.

MARK: Okay, Ms. Potter.

SALLY: I promise, Ms. Potter. Phew!

MARK: Boy!

41.4 TRY A LITTLE HARDER—
Music Video (8:36)

Let's say you're a driver,
A careful driver who
Drives very carefully,
As careful drivers do.
Just try a little harder.
You can find a way.
Try to drive more carefully today.

Let's say you're a singer,
A beautiful singer who
Sings very beautifully,
As beautiful singers do.
Just try a little harder.
You can find a way.
Try to sing more beautifully today.

Let's say you're a dancer,
A graceful dancer who
Dances very gracefully,
As graceful dancers do.
Try a little harder.
You can find a way.
Try to dance more gracefully today.

Just try a little harder.
That's what we always say.
Sing a little stronger.
Work a little longer.
Do a little better.
Every day.
(Do a little better every day . . .
    Yeah!!!)

GRAMMAR

Adverbs

	slowly. terribly. sloppily.
He works	
	fast. hard. well.

Comparatives of Adverbs

	more neatly. neater.
He should try to work	more carefully. more politely.
	faster. harder. better.

Agent Nouns

driver singer actor painter dancer reporter player

FUNCTIONS

Describing

He's a *careless driver*.

He *drives* very *carelessly/slowly/ fast/well . . .*

Expressing an Opinion

He should *try to speak slower.*

I think *George dresses very sloppily.*

It's a *bad* idea.

You're wrong.

Expressing Agreement

I agree.
I think so.
You're right.
He sure *is.*
I'll say.
I know.

Expressing Disagreement

I don't agree with you, *Mr. Jenkins.*

Surprise

Boy!

Leave Taking

See you later.
Bye.
Have a nice day, *Edith.*

Greeting People

Hi, *Sally.*

Hello *Mark.* How are you doing?
    I'm fine, *Francine.*
    Everything's great, *Francine.*

Expressing Disappointment

I'm very disappointed.

Expressing Regret

Sorry, *Ms. Potter.*

I apologize, *Ms. Potter.*

SEGMENT 42

- **If-Clauses**
- **Consequences of Actions**

"If it rains, we'll sit and talk. If it's nice, we'll take a walk . . . Side by Side."

LESSON MENU

SBS-TV Backstage Bulletin Board

TO: Production Crew
Sets and props for this segment:

Bedroom and Office
bed
telephones
desk
chair

Kitchen
table
chairs
coffee cups

Car
steering wheel
candy bar
cellular phone
radio

TO: Cast Members
Key words in this segment:

feel better
baby
due

superstitions
good luck
bad luck

if
will
might
shouldn't

so
too
so much
too much

42.1 I'M AFRAID I WON'T BE AT WORK TODAY (11:09)

YES OR NO?

1 Mrs. Carter is calling Donald.	Yes	(No)
2 It's afternoon.	Yes	No
3 Donald is going to work today.	Yes	No
4 Donald has a bad cold.	Yes	No
5 Mrs. Carter is sorry Donald has a cold.	Yes	No
6 If he feels better tomorrow, he'll stay home.	Yes	No

7 If he's still sick tomorrow, he'll probably go to the doctor.   Yes   No

8 If he can't come to work tomorrow, Mrs. Carter will call him.   Yes   No

9 Mrs. Carter hopes Donald feels better soon.   Yes   No

10 Mrs. Carter says Donald should go to the doctor.   Yes   No

11 Donald thanks Mrs. Carter for calling.   Yes   No

SOUND CHECK

Donald has a bad cold and can't come to work today. Put a circle around what Donald says.

1 If ⟨I feel / I'll feel⟩ better tomorrow, ⟨I come / I'll come⟩ to work.

2 If I ⟨won't / don't⟩ feel better, ⟨I probably go / I'll probably go⟩ to the doctor.

3 If ⟨I'll can't / I can't⟩ come to work tomorrow, ⟨I'll call / I call⟩ you.

WHAT ARE THEY SAYING?

Circle the lines you hear.

1 a. So what are you going to do?

   (b.) So what's new with you?

2 a. I have some exciting news.

   b. I bought something new.

3 a. What's that?

   b. Where's that?

4 a. I'm going there with my grandmother!

   b. I'm going to be a grandmother!

5 a. When is it due?

   b. What are you going to do?

6 a. In December.

   b. In September.

7 a. When are they going to name their new baby?

   b. What are they going to name their new baby?

8 a. If they have a boy, they'll name him John.

   b. If they have a boy, they'll name him Tom.

9 a. If they have a girl, they'll name her Mame.

   b. If they have a girl, they'll name her Jane.

10 a. I'm so happy it's true.

   b. I'm so happy for you.

SOUND CHECK

1 If they'll have / (they have) a boy, they name / they'll name him John.

2 If they'll have / they have a girl, they name / they'll name her Jane.

GIFT IDEAS

What do you think the new grandmother will give her grandchild when it's born? Put a circle around the correct answers and then complete the sentences.

1 If (it's) / it'll be a boy, she give / she'll give him ....

2 If it'll be / it's a girl, she'll give / she give her ....

42.3 SBS-TV ON LOCATION (12:25)

What are you going to do this weekend?

If the weather ~~will be~~ (is) [1] good, ~~I work~~ I'll work [2] outside in my yard.

If the weather ~~will be~~ is [3] bad, ~~I'll~~ I [4] probably clean my basement.

I guess it depends on the weather. If ~~it'll be~~ it's [5] sunny,

~~I go~~ I'll go [6] for a long bike ride. If ~~it'll rain~~ it rains [7],

~~I~~ I'll [8] most likely go to a movie.

If ~~I have~~ I'll have [9] a lot of homework, ~~I'll stay~~ I stay [10] home and study.

If ~~I won't~~ I don't [11] have a lot of homework, ~~I~~ I'll [12] probably get together with my friends.

You're on Side by Side TV! Tell the viewers about your plans for the weekend.

What are you going to do this weekend if the weather is nice?

....

....

What are you going to do this weekend if the weather is bad?

....

....

Listen to Aunt Gertrude's advice and fill in the correct verbs.

might	drive	get	hit	park	stay
shouldn't	eat	have	hurt	play	talk

You know . . . you ____shouldn't____ ____drive____ ¹
so fast. If you _____² too fast, you
_____ _____³ an accident.

You know . . . you _____ _____ ⁴
so much candy. If you _____⁵ too much candy,
you _____ _____⁶ a toothache.

You know . . . you really _____ _____ ⁷
on your car phone when you're driving. If you
_____⁸ on your car phone when you're
driving, you _____ _____ ⁹
somebody.

You know . . . you _____ _____ ¹⁰
your car radio so loud. If you _____¹¹
your radio too loud, you _____
_____¹² your ears.

You know, Sherman . . . if you _____¹³ too
close to that fire hydrant, you _____
_____¹⁴ a ticket.

You know . . . I'm so happy to be here, I think I
_____ _____¹⁵ for a
month. Or maybe TWO months.

SHERMAN'S MOODS

*In this scene Sherman sometimes looks and sounds **pleasant**, sometimes **annoyed**, sometimes **angry**, and sometimes **sad**. Watch Sherman and decide how he looks and sounds when he and Aunt Gertrude say the following lines.*

(pleasant)   annoyed

1 GERTRUDE: "It was nice of you to pick me up at the bus station, Sherman."

SHERMAN: "My pleasure, Aunt Gertrude. We're all happy you can visit us for a few days."

pleasant   annoyed

2 GERTRUDE: "If you drive too fast, you might have an accident."

SHERMAN: "Hmm. You're probably right."

pleasant   annoyed

3 GERTRUDE: "If you eat too much candy, you might get a toothache."

SHERMAN: "You're probably right, Aunt Gertrude."

pleasant   annoyed

4 GERTRUDE: "If you talk on your car phone when you're driving, you might hit somebody."

SHERMAN: "You're probably right, Aunt Gertrude."

annoyed   angry

5 GERTRUDE: "If you play your radio too loud, you might hurt your ears."

SHERMAN: "You're right, Aunt Gertrude. You're absolutely right."

annoyed   angry

6 GERTRUDE: "If you park too close to that fire hydrant, you might get a ticket."

SHERMAN: "There, Aunt Gertrude. How's that?"

angry   sad

7 GERTRUDE: "That's fine, Sherman. Good job! You know . . . I'm so happy to be here, I think I might stay for a month. Or maybe TWO months."

GOOD ADVICE

Write your advice for these people.

1. Eric has a big exam tomorrow, and he isn't studying. He's watching TV.

2. Maggie is a very successful businesswoman, but she works 16 hours a day and never relaxes.

3. Linda snacks on junk food all day.

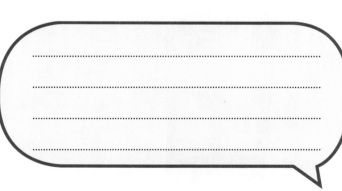

4. Harry hates to exercise, and he's gaining a lot of weight.

SCRAMBLED SOUND TRACK

The sound track is all mixed up! Put the words in the correct order.

1 | four-leaf | good | If | you'll | you | luck. | clover, | find | have | a

If you find a four-leaf clover, you'll have good luck.

_____

2 | house, | you'll | luck. | open | bad | If | an | umbrella | your | you | in | have

_____

_____

3 | you'll | for | you | have | seven | break | bad | years. | a | If | mirror, | luck

_____

_____

4 | your | itches, | saying | about | right | somebody | good | you. | If | ear | is | things

_____

_____

5 | about | bad | is | itches, | left | If | you. | saying | ear | somebody | your | things

_____

_____

6 | find | you'll | luck. | horseshoe, | If | a | have | you | good

_____

_____

EDITING MIX-UP

The video editor made a mistake! Put the following lines in the correct order.

_____ No. I'm not superstitious at all.

__1__ Superstitions? I don't believe any of that stuff.

_____ Yes?

_____ You know . . . some people believe that if you walk under a ladder, you'll have bad luck.

_____ Hmm. Do you see that ladder?

_____ Whatever you say!

_____ Well, I gotta get going now. Nice talking with you.

_____ That's ridiculous!

_____ You aren't superstitious?

CLOSE-UP

You're on Side by Side TV! Tell the viewers about a superstition you know.

....

....

....

SUPERSTITION SURVEY

Ask four friends about superstitions they know, and fill out the superstition survey form.

Friend's Name	Superstition
Sally	If a black cat walks in front of you, you'll have bad luck.
1.	
2.	
3.	
4.	

TOO MUCH ADVICE!

Johnny thinks he gets too much advice! All day long his parents, his teacher, and even his big brother tell him what to do. What do they say to him?

You know, Johnny, you _____*shouldn't*_____[1] stay up so late! If you _____*stay*_____[2] up too late, you ____*might*____ ___*be*___[3] tired tomorrow! And you _____[4] play your radio so loud! If you _____[5] your radio too loud, Grandpa and Grandma _____ _____[6] upset! And you _____[7] forget to do your chores! If you _____[8] to do your chores, we'll be upset!

You know, Johnny, you _____[9] forget to do your homework! If you _____[10] to do your homework, you _____[11] get a bad grade on the test! And you _____[12] talk to your friends so much in class! If you _____[13] too much to your friends in class, you _____[14] forget your homework! And remember, you _____[15] be late for school so often! If _____[16] late for school too often, you _____[17] have to go to the principal's office!

You know, Johnny, you _____[18] read so late at night! If you _____[19] too late at night, you _____ _____[20] tired at school tomorrow! And if _____[21] too tired at school tomorrow, you _____[22] fall asleep at your desk! And, you _____[23] throw your clothes on the floor! If you _____[24] your clothes on the floor, I _____[25] walk on them and get them dirty!

••••• SEGMENT 42

42.1 I'M AFRAID I WON'T BE AT WORK TODAY (11:09)

MRS. CARTER:	Mrs. Carter.
DONALD:	Hello, Mrs. Carter. This is Donald Hopkins.
MRS. CARTER:	Good morning, Donald.
DONALD:	Mrs. Carter, I'm afraid I won't be at work today. I have a very bad cold.
MRS. CARTER:	That's too bad, Donald. I'm sorry to hear that.
DONALD:	If I feel better tomorrow, I'll come to work. If I don't feel better, I'll probably go to the doctor.
MRS. CARTER:	That's fine, Donald.
DONALD:	If I can't come to work tomorrow, I'll call you.
MRS. CARTER:	Thank you very much, Donald. I hope you feel better soon.
DONALD:	Thank you, Mrs. Carter. Good-bye.
MRS. CARTER:	Bye.

42.2 I'M GOING TO BE A GRANDMOTHER! (11:50)

FRIEND 1:	So what's new with you?
FRIEND 2:	Well, actually, I have some exciting news.
FRIEND 1:	What's that?
FRIEND 2:	I'm going to be a grandmother! Melanie and her husband are going to have a baby.
FRIEND 1:	That's terrific! When is it due?
FRIEND 2:	In September.
FRIEND 1:	What are they going to name their new baby?
FRIEND 2:	If they have a boy, they'll name him John. If they have a girl, they'll name her Jane.
FRIEND 1:	Well, that's really wonderful. I'm so happy for you.

42.3 SBS-TV ON LOCATION (12:25)

INTERVIEWER: What are you going to do this weekend?

PERSON 1: I'm not sure. If the weather is good, I'll work outside in my yard. If the weather is bad, I'll probably clean my basement.

PERSON 2: This weekend? I guess it depends on the weather. If it's sunny, I'll go for a long bike ride. If it rains, I'll most likely go to a movie.

PERSON 3: Gee, I don't know. If I have a lot of homework, I'll stay home and study. If I don't have a lot of homework, I'll probably get together with my friends.

42.4 YOU SHOULDN'T DRIVE SO FAST! (12:53)

AUNT GERTRUDE: It was nice of you to pick me up at the bus station, Sherman.

SHERMAN: My pleasure, Aunt Gertrude. We're all happy you can visit us for a few days.

AUNT GERTRUDE: Uh . . . Sherman?

SHERMAN: Yes, Aunt Gertrude?

AUNT GERTRUDE: You know . . . you shouldn't drive so fast.

SHERMAN: Oh?

AUNT GERTRUDE: Yes. If you drive too fast, you might have an accident.

SHERMAN: Hmm. You're probably right.

(Sherman starts to eat a candy bar.)

AUNT GERTRUDE: Sherman?

SHERMAN: Yes, Aunt Gertrude?

AUNT GERTRUDE: You know . . . you shouldn't eat so much candy.

SHERMAN: Oh?

AUNT GERTRUDE: Yes. If you eat too much candy, you might get a toothache.

SHERMAN: You're probably right, Aunt Gertrude.

(Sherman answers his car phone.)

SHERMAN: Hello. Hi, Paula. Yes. I met her at the bus station, and we're on our way home right now. In about five minutes. Bye.

AUNT GERTRUDE: You know, Sherman . . . you really shouldn't talk on your car phone when you're driving.

SHERMAN: Oh?

AUNT GERTRUDE: Yes. If you talk on your car phone when you're driving, you might hit somebody.

SHERMAN: You're probably right, Aunt Gertrude.

(Sherman turns on the radio.)

AUNT GERTRUDE: Sherman! Sherman!! Sherman?!

SHERMAN: Yes, Aunt Gertrude.

AUNT GERTRUDE: You know . . . you shouldn't play your car radio so loud.

SHERMAN: Oh?

AUNT GERTRUDE: Yes. If you play your radio too loud, you might hurt your ears.

SHERMAN: You're right, Aunt Gertrude. You're absolutely right.

(Sherman parks the car.)

SHERMAN: Well, we're here, Aunt Gertrude.

AUNT GERTRUDE: You know, Sherman . . . If you park too close to that fire hydrant, you might get a ticket.

(Sherman parks a little better.)

SHERMAN: There, Aunt Gertrude. How's that?

AUNT GERTRUDE: That's fine, Sherman. Good job! You know . . . I'm so happy to be here, I think I might stay for a month. Or maybe TWO months.

42.5 SBS-TV ON LOCATION (15:50)

INTERVIEWER: Do you know any superstitions?

PERSON 1: Yes. If you find a four-leaf clover, you'll have good luck.

INTERVIEWER: Do you believe that?

PERSON 1: I sure do. Here. Let me show you. You see this? This is my four-leaf clover. I carry it all the time.

PERSON 2: Superstitions? Hmm. I can think of one. If you open an umbrella in your house, you'll have bad luck.

PERSON 3: If you break a mirror, you'll have bad luck for seven years.

PERSON 4: If your right ear itches, somebody is saying good things about you. If your left ear itches, somebody is saying bad things about you.

PERSON 5: Do I know any superstitions? Hmm. I can't think of any. Wait a minute! I know one. If you find a horseshoe, you'll have good luck.

PERSON 6: Superstitions? I don't believe any of that stuff.

INTERVIEWER: You aren't superstitious?

PERSON 6: No. I'm not superstitious at all.

INTERVIEWER: Hmm. Do you see that ladder?

PERSON 6: Yes?

INTERVIEWER: You know . . . some people believe that if you walk under a ladder, you'll have bad luck.

PERSON 6: That's ridiculous!

INTERVIEWER: Whatever you say!

PERSON 6: Well, I gotta get going now. Nice talking with you.

(Somebody drops a plant from a window.)

WOMAN: Oh sorry, young man! Are you okay?

GRAMMAR

If-Clauses

If	I we you they / he she	feel / feels	better,	I'll we'll you'll they'll / he'll she'll	go to work.

FUNCTIONS

Expressing Inability

I'm afraid I won't be *at work today.*

Expressing Sympathy

I'm sorry to hear that.

Expressing a Wish

I hope you *feel better soon.*

Asking for and Reporting Information

What's new with you? *Well, actually, I have some exciting news.*

Do you know *any superstitions?*

Congratulating

That's terrific!

Expressing Intention

If *they have a boy,* they'll *name him John.*
If *it's sunny,* I'll *go for a bike ride.*

Inquiring about Intention

What are you going to do *this weekend?*

Initiating a Topic

You know, . . .

Expressing Certainty-Uncertainty

I'm not sure.

I guess *it depends on the weather.*

I don't know.

Gratitude

It was nice of you *to pick me up at the bus station, Sherman.*

Offering Advice

You shouldn't *drive so fast.*

Expressing Possibility

If you *drive too fast,* you might *have an accident.*

Expressing Agreement

You're probably right.
You're right.
You're absolutely right.

Asking for an Opinion

Do you believe *that?*

Expressing an Opinion

I don't believe *any of that stuff.*

SEGMENT 43

- **Past Continuous Tense**
- **Describing Past Activities**

"I was cleaning. You were cooking. He was playing.

They were looking . . . Side by Side."

LESSON MENU

SBS-TV Backstage Bulletin Board

TO: Production Crew
Sets and props for this segment:

News Studio
desk
clock

Exterior
microphone

Doctor's Office
eye chart
eye glasses

Living Room
chairs
coat
book
lamp

TO: Cast Members
Key words in this segment:

blackout
batteries
power company
controls

taxi

jogging

tenants
robbery
break into
burglar

Well, as you all know by now, there was a blackout in Centerville last night. The lights went out all over town.

Side by Side TV News Reporter Scott Mason is standing by downtown to find out what people were doing last night when the lights went out. Scott, are you there?

Jackie, it seems like everybody in town is talking about the blackout last night. Everyone has a story to tell.

SOUND CHECK

| was | were | do | give | wash | watch |

What _____were_____ [1] YOU _____doing_____ [2] last night when the lights went out?

I _____ [3] the dishes, and my wife _____ [4] the baby a bath.

I _____ [5] my clothes at the laundromat, and suddenly everything got dark!

My husband and I _____ [6] TV, and our children _____ [7] their homework.

EDITING MIX-UP

The video editor made a mistake! Put the following lines in the correct order.

_____ You were listening to music? But there was no electricity!

_____ Did the lights go out last night?

__1__ Excuse me!

_____ Yes! The lights went out all over town!

_____ Yeah?

_____ Huh! How about that! I didn't even know! I was listening to music all night!

_____ What were you doing last night when the lights went out?

_____ Batteries!

ON CAMERA

You're a reporter for Side by Side TV. Interview these people and complete their answers any way you wish.

What were YOU doing last night when the lights went out?

1

2

3

4

YES OR NO?

1	Gloria Rodriguez is at the Power Company.	(Yes)	No
2	Fred Watts is the Director of Public Transportation for the Power Company.	Yes	No
3	The weather was bad during the blackout.	Yes	No
4	Fred Watts is sure that's why the blackout took place.	Yes	No
5	According to Gloria Rodriguez, they were having a big party last night and nobody was watching the controls.	Yes	No
6	Fred Watts says they were working then.	Yes	No

WHAT DO YOU THINK?

Do you think Fred Watts is telling the truth? ....

What is Gloria Rodriguez thinking? ....

What is Fred Watts thinking? ....

In your opinion, why did the lights go out last night? ....

WHAT WAS EVERYBODY DOING?

1 When the lights went out, Bob Rogers was _____.

   a. watching TV

   (b.) washing the dishes

2 Bob's wife was _____.

   a. taking a bath

   b. studying math

3 Jackie Williams was _____.

   a. sitting and knitting

   b. working in the building

4 The station manager and his wife, Mr. and Mrs. Green, were _____.

   a. riding in the elevator

   b. buying a refrigerator

43.2 OUR NEIGHBORS, OUR LIVES (20:45)

WHAT'S HAPPENING?

1 She saw him, _____.
- a. and he saw her, too
- (b.) but he didn't see her

2 It was at about _____.
- a. 2:30
- b. 3:30

3 According to _____, he was getting out of a taxi.
- a. him
- b. her

4 The taxi was on _____.
- a. Main Street
- b. Blaine Street

5 He says he was _____.
- a. cooking dinner
- b. eating dinner

6 _____ made a mistake.
- a. He
- b. She

WHAT DO YOU THINK?

Who are these people? ....

What is their relationship? ....

Is he telling her the truth? ....

Does she believe him? ....

What really happened? ....

CONTINUE THE SCENE!

What happens on the next episode of "Our Neighbors, Our Lives?" Write the script and then practice it with a friend.

A. ....

B. ....

A. ....

B. ....

A. ....

B. ....

43.3 "I SEE YOU" OPTICIANS (21:18)

1 Ernesto Retina is ____ "I See You" Opticians.

   a. the owner of

   b. going to

2 People who have trouble with their ____ go there.

   a. ears

   b. eyes

3 In the scene at the office, one person says he ____ the other.

   a. called

   b. saw

4 It was at about ____.

   a. 2:00

   b. 4:00

5 He says the other person was ____.

   a. jogging through the park

   b. driving a car

6 The other person says ____.

   a. that's true

   b. that's not true

7 He says he was ____.

   a. playing tennis

   b. paying the rent

8 The person made a mistake because ____.

   a. he's jealous

   b. he can't see very well

9 Ernesto Retina says, "____!"

   a. 'I See You' is the store for you

   b. I'll see you at 'I See You'

10 This scene was ____.

   a. true

   b. a commercial

MATCH!

Complete each of these sentences.

___d___ **1** I saw Bob this morning, ____.

_____ **2** I saw you today at about ____.

_____ **3** When I saw Carla, ____.

_____ **4** I guess I ____.

_____ **5** I'll see you ____.

a. made a mistake

b. at "I See You"

c. 3:45

d. but he didn't see me

e. she was walking down Main Street

SOUND CHECK

| was | were | wash | visit | have | play | attend | do |

Yesterday wasn't a very good day for the people who live at 151 River Street. Burglars broke into every apartment in the building while all the tenants were out.

What __were__ [1] you folks __doing__ [2] yesterday afternoon?

I _____ _____ [3] my clothes at the laundromat.

I _____ _____ [4] a friend in the hospital.

We _____ _____ [5] a picnic at the beach.

I _____ _____ [6] tennis in the park.

My roommate and I _____ _____ [7] a football game.

I _____ _____ [8] my grandchildren in Ohio.

Today everybody is trying to put their apartments —and their lives—back together. Maxine Baxter, Side by Side TV News.

WRITE THE SCRIPT!

The police found a witness to the robbery at 151 River Street yesterday afternoon. Finish the script and then practice it with a friend.

POLICE OFFICER: Tell me, what did you see yesterday afternoon on River Street?

WITNESS: Well, . . . a man and a woman _____were entering_____[1] 151 River Street at
(enter)

about two o'clock in the afternoon.

POLICE OFFICER: What _____[2] they _____[3]?
(do)

WITNESS: The woman _____[4] a big yellow bag, and I think the
(carry)

man _____[5] the door to see if people
(watch)

_____[6] at them.
(look)

POLICE OFFICER: Did they see you?

WITNESS: No. I _____[7] behind the mailbox on the corner with my dog.
(stand)

POLICE OFFICER: Why didn't your dog bark?

WITNESS: My dog? He _____[8] at the cat in the window of one of
(look)

the apartments.

POLICE OFFICER: I see. Can you give me a description of the two suspects?

 42

WITNESS: Certainly. The woman was tall, and she _____ ⁹ a blue
(wear)

blouse and white pants. The man _____ ¹⁰ a black shirt
(wear)

and jeans. Also, the man _____ ¹¹ a large radio.
(hold)

POLICE OFFICER: Were there other people around at that time?

WITNESS: Yes. Two children _____ ¹² basketball in the park.
(play)

A woman _____ ¹³ a baby carriage. A young man
(push)

_____ ¹⁴ down the street, and the mail
(jog)

carrier _____ ¹⁵ mail next door. A young boy
(deliver)

_____ ¹⁶ to music in the park across the street,
(listen)

and a woman _____ ¹⁷ flowers in the yard next door.
(plant)

POLICE OFFICER: Did you see anybody suspicious?

WITNESS: Hmm. Yes, I think so. A man and a woman _____ ¹⁸
(sit)

in a car across the street. They _____ ¹⁹ the apartment
(watch)

building very carefully.

POLICE OFFICER: What did the two people in the car do after the suspects left the apartment
building?

WITNESS: They _____ ²⁰ and _____ ²¹ the car's
(drive away)   (honk)

horn several times.

POLICE OFFICER: What kind of car _____ ²² they _____ ²³?
(have)

WITNESS: They _____ ²⁴ a big green car with a thin white strip on the side.
(have)

POLICE OFFICER: Is that all you can remember?

WITNESS: Yes, I think so.

POLICE OFFICER: Well, thank you for all your help.

WITNESS: My pleasure.

DO YOU REMEMBER?

How many facts about the robbery do you remember?

1. The robbery was at _____. a. 161 River Street (b.) 151 River Street
2. One tenant was _____. a. washing clothes b. buying clothes
3. Another was visiting a friend _____. a. in the hospital b. in Boston
4. Another tenant was having a picnic _____. a. in the park b. at the beach
5. One was playing _____. a. tennis b. volleyball
6. Another was attending _____. a. a baseball game b. a football game
7. A woman was visiting her _____. a. grandmother b. grandchildren
8. According to a witness, it all took place _____. a. at about 3:00 b. at about 2:00
9. The witness saw the woman carrying _____. a. a yellow bag b. a big suitcase
10. A man was _____. a. watching her b. watching the door
11. The witness's dog was looking at _____. a. a car b. a cat
12. The woman was wearing _____. a. a white blouse b. a blue blouse
13. The man was wearing _____. a. jeans b. a black suit
14. The man was holding _____. a. a large yellow bag b. a radio
15. Two children nearby were playing _____. a. a radio b. basketball

WHAT WERE THEY DOING?

What verb do each of the following pairs of words have in common? Write a question with the verb. There may be more than one possible question.

1. tennis
   the piano   *What were they playing?* _____

2. the dishes
   their car   _____

3. music
   the radio   _____

4. breakfast
   dinner   _____

5. TV
   a video   _____

6. the rent
   a bill   _____

SEGMENT 43 SCRIPT ●●●

43.1 MORNING EDITION (17:19)

ANNOUNCER: This is Side by Side TV News, Morning Edition, with Bob Rogers and Jackie Williams, Maria Hernandez with the weather, and Chip Stevens on sports.

BOB ROGERS: Good morning, everybody. Along with Jackie Williams, I'm Bob Rogers. Well, as you all know by now, there was a blackout in Centerville last night. The lights went out all over town.

JACKIE WILLIAMS: Side by Side TV News Reporter Scott Mason is standing by downtown to find out what people were doing last night when the lights went out. Scott, are you there?

SCOTT MASON: Jackie, it seems like everybody in town is talking about the blackout last night. Everyone has a story to tell. What were YOU doing last night when the lights went out?

PERSON 1: I was washing the dishes, and my wife was giving the baby a bath.

PERSON 2: I was washing my clothes at the laundromat, and suddenly everything got dark!

PERSON 3: My husband and I were watching TV, and our children were doing their homework.

SCOTT MASON: And what were YOU doing last night when the lights went out? Excuse me!

PERSON 4: Yeah?

SCOTT MASON: What were you doing last night when the lights went out?

PERSON 4: Did the lights go out last night?

SCOTT MASON: Yes! The lights went out all over town!

PERSON 4: Huh! How about that! I didn't even know! I was listening to music all night!

SCOTT MASON: You were listening to music? But there was no electricity!

PERSON 4: Batteries!

SCOTT MASON: So you see, Bob and Jackie, everybody's talking about what they were doing last night when the lights went out. But why did the lights go out? To find the answer, Side by Side TV News Reporter Gloria Rodriguez is standing by at the main office of the power company. Gloria?

GLORIA RODRIGUEZ: I'm here at the main office of the Centerville Power Company with Fred Watts, the company's director of public information. Mr. Watts, what happened last night?

FRED WATTS: Well, Gloria, as you know, the lights went out all over town.

GLORIA RODRIGUEZ: Yes, we know that, Mr. Watts. Can you tell us why?

FRED WATTS:	Well, we aren't sure yet. We know it was raining very hard when the blackout occurred, but we aren't certain that's the reason for the problem. We're working on it.
GLORIA RODRIGUEZ:	Mr. Watts, is it true that you were all having a big party here last night and nobody was watching the controls?
FRED WATTS:	Absolutely not! We were working here and doing our jobs as usual.
GLORIA RODRIGUEZ:	Well, thank you for talking with us, Mr. Watts. So, Bob and Jackie, that's what we know right now. It was raining very hard last night, and perhaps that's the reason the lights went out all over town. This is Gloria Rodriguez, reporting live from the power company, for Side by Side TV News.
JACKIE WILLIAMS:	Thank you, Gloria. Phew! What a night! What were YOU doing last night when the lights went out?
BOB ROGERS:	I was washing the dishes.
JACKIE WILLIAMS:	How about your wife? What was Doris doing last night when the lights went out?
BOB ROGERS:	She was taking a bath.
JACKIE WILLIAMS:	I was still working in the building. Did you hear what happened to the station manager and his wife?
BOB ROGERS:	No. What were Mr. and

	Mrs. Green doing last night when the lights went out?
JACKIE WILLIAMS:	They were riding in the elevator.
BOB ROGERS:	Oh. That's terrible!
JACKIE WILLIAMS:	Coming up, a robbery on River Street. We'll be back in a moment.

43.2 OUR NEIGHBORS, OUR LIVES (20:45)

WOMAN:	I saw you yesterday, but you didn't see me.
MAN:	Really? When?
WOMAN:	At about 2:30. You were getting out of a taxi on Main Street.
MAN:	That wasn't me. Yesterday at 2:30 I was cooking dinner.
WOMAN:	Hmm. I guess I made a mistake.
ANNOUNCER:	Stay tuned for *Our Neighbors, Our Lives,* coming up after the morning news.

43.3 "I SEE YOU" OPTICIANS (21:18)

ERNESTO RETINA:	Hi. This is Ernesto Retina, owner of "I See You," your

46

one-stop place for eye examinations and eyeglasses. Does this scene look familiar?

CO-WORKER 1: I saw you yesterday, but you didn't see me.

CO-WORKER 2: Really? When?

CO-WORKER 1: At about four o'clock. You were jogging through the park.

CO-WORKER 2: That wasn't me. Yesterday at four o'clock I was playing tennis.

CO-WORKER 1: Hmm. I guess I made a mistake.

ERNESTO RETINA: Don't let this happen to you. Come to "I See You" for an eye examination today. This is Ernesto Retina, saying, I'll see you at "I See You."

43.4 MORNING EDITION–Continued

(22:10)

BOB ROGERS: There was a robbery at 151 River Street yesterday afternoon. Side by Side TV News Reporter Maxine Baxter talked with the tenants of the building and filed this report.

MAXINE BAXTER: Yesterday wasn't a very good day for the people who live at 151 River Street. Burglars broke into every apartment in the building while all the tenants were out. What were you folks doing yesterday afternoon?

TENANT 1: I was washing my clothes at the laundromat.

TENANT 2: I was visiting a friend in the hospital.

TENANT 3: We were having a picnic at the beach.

TENANT 4: I was playing tennis in the park.

MAXINE BAXTER: And how about you? What were you doing?

TENANT 5: My roommate and I were attending a football game.

TENANT 6: I was out of town. I was visiting my grandchildren in Ohio.

MAXINE BAXTER: And how do you all feel about what happened?

TENANT 3: I'm really upset!

TENANT 4: It's terrible!

TENANT 2: I can't believe it!

MAXINE BAXTER: Yesterday certainly was an unfortunate day for the people at 151 River Street. They had no idea that while they were away, burglars broke into every apartment in the building. Today everybody is trying to put their apartments— and their lives—back together. Maxine Baxter, Side by Side TV News.

JACKIE WILLIAMS: Police are still investigating the robbery at 151 River Street. As of now, there are no suspects.

BOB ROGERS: And that's the Side by Side TV News Morning Edition for today. We'll see you this evening. I'm Bob Rogers.

JACKIE WILLIAMS: And I'm Jackie Williams. *Our Neighbors, Our Lives* is next. Have a good day!

GRAMMAR

Past Continuous Tense

What	was	I he she it	doing?
	were	we you they	

I He She It	was	eating.
We You They	were	

FUNCTIONS

Asking for and Reporting Information

What were you doing *last night at 8:00?*
What was *Doris* doing *last night* when *the
    lights went out?*

I saw *you yesterday.*
    When?
At about *4:00.*

Yesterday at *4:00* I was *playing tennis.*

Which *apartment* do you live in?
    Apartment 1.

Were you *home at the time of the robbery?*
    No, I wasn't. I was *washing my clothes
    at the laundromat.*

Sympathizing

Oh. That's terrible.

Initiating a Topic

Excuse me.

Greeting People

Good morning, *everybody.*

Expressing Disbelief

Huh! How about that?

Really?

I can't believe it!

Expressing Uncertainty

We *aren't* sure yet.

Denying

Absolutely not!

Gratitude

Thank you, *Gloria.*

Warning

Don't *let this happen to you.*

Expressing Anxiety

I'm really upset!

It's terrible!

SEGMENT 44

- **Reflexive Pronouns**
- **While-Clauses**
- **Past Continuous Tense**
- **Describing Past Activities**

"He took his razor from the shelf, and then while shaving cut himself . . . Side by Side."

LESSON MENU

SBS-TV Backstage Bulletin Board

TO: Production Crew
Sets and props for this segment:

Offices
coffee cups
chair
desk

Kitchen
cards
table
chair

Bedroom
bed

Movie
chair
popcorn

Outside
paint brush
paint sprayer

Clinic
counter
telephone
chairs

TO: Cast Members
Key words in this segment:

myself
yourself
himself
herself
itself
ourselves
yourselves
themselves

burn
cut
hurt
paint
poke
slice

44.1 BY THEMSELVES (24:16)

1 He went to the _____ yesterday.
- a. museum
- b. beach ⟵(circled)

2 He says, "I went by _____."
- a. himself
- b. myself

3 She says, "You went by _____?"
- a. yourself
- b. myself

4 He had a _____ time.
- a. bad
- b. good

5 John went to the _____ yesterday.
- a. movies
- b. zoo

6 He went by _____.
- a. myself
- b. himself

7 _____ went with him.
- a. A friend
- b. Nobody

8 He ate _____ while he was watching the movie.
- a. pizza
- b. popcorn

9 Tina played _____ yesterday.
- a. darts
- b. cards

10 She played by _____.
- a. herself
- b. myself

11 _____ played with her.
- a. Nobody
- b. Somebody

12 She played in the _____.
- a. dining room
- b. kitchen

SCENE CHECK

1 The Robinsons are painting their house by _____.

   a. themself

   b. themselves

2 The Robinsons' first names are _____.

   a. Lois and Harry

   b. Lois and Larry

3 They say, "We're painting it _____."

   a. ourselves

   b. themselves

4 The paint sprayer can almost paint the house by _____.

   a. itself

   b. himself

5 The wife thinks they should paint their house by _____.

   a. ourselves

   b. themselves

6 The husband asks, "By _____?"

   a. ourselves

   b. themselves

7 She says, "They're doing it _____."

   a. ourselves

   b. themselves

8 The husband says, "All right. _____."

   a. I agree

   b. We'll see

SCRIPT CHECK

Watch the scene and check the number of times you hear each of the following:

itself	ourselves	yourselves	themselves
l			

Total   1   _____   _____   _____

44.3 THEY HAD A BAD DAY TODAY (25:45)

EDITING MIX-UP

The video editor made a mistake! Put the following lines in the correct order.

1

2

____ Why? What happened?

____ I'm sorry to hear that.

____ I lost my wallet while I was jogging through the park.

_1_ You look upset.

____ I had a bad day today.

____ He had a bad day today.

____ Harry looks upset.

____ He cut himself while he was shaving.

____ Why? What happened?

____ What a shame!

BAD DAYS

Ask five friends about a bad day they had. What happened to them? What were they doing when it happened?

Friend's Name	What happened?
Sally	She slipped on the ice while she was walking to work.
1.	
2.	
3.	
4.	
5.	

CLOSE-UP

You're on Side by Side TV! Tell about a bad day you had.

....

....

44.4 THE REFLEXIVE INJURY CLINIC (26:20)

SOUND CHECK

What happened to these people? Circle the words you hear.

1	hurt	(burned)	**2**	hurt	burned	**3**	poke	poked	**4**	caught	cut
	myself	himself		himself	myself		myself	himself		herself	himself
	will	while		will	while		ear	eye		will	while
	dinner	lunch		rowing	bowling		Ouch!	Wow!		slicing	splicing

THE NEXT LINE

Circle the correct response.

1 What did you do?

  a. That's too bad.

  (b.) I burned myself.

2 How about you?

  a. I'm sorry to hear that.

  b. I hurt myself.

3 Your back?

  a. I came back yesterday.

  b. Yeah . . . my back.

4 What's the matter with your husband?

  a. That's too bad.

  b. He poked himself in the eye.

5 Ouch! I bet that hurts!

  a. Oh, no!

  b. It sure does!

6 What happened to your daughter?

  a. She cut a bagel.

  b. She cut herself.

7 Is this your first time here?

  a. Oh, no.

  b. Ouch!

8 Was he angry?

  a. Oh, yes! He was beside himself!

  b. Oh, yes! He hurt himself!

MISSING LINES

The nurse is on the telephone. What do you think the other person is saying? Complete the lines and then practice the telephone conversation with a friend.

NURSE: Reflexive Injury Clinic.

CALLER: ....

NURSE: Uh-húh.

CALLER: ....

NURSE: Uh-húh.

CALLER: ....

NURSE: It's broken?

CALLER: ....

NURSE: I see. And did you do this to yourself, or did it just happen?

CALLER: ....

NURSE: I see. Well, I'm sorry. I'm afraid we can't help you. We only take care of REFLEXIVE injuries.

CALLER: ....

NURSE: That's right. Things people do to themselves, like when they cut themselves, burn themselves, or hurt themselves.

CALLER: ....

NURSE: I'm sorry to hear it's broken, but I'm afraid we can't help you.

CALLER: ....

NURSE: Well, take care of yourself!

CALLER: ....

NURSE: Good-bye.

ON CAMERA

*You're the receptionist! Answer the telephone and decide which injuries are **reflexive** and can be treated at the Reflexive Injury Clinic. Circle **Yes** or **No**.*

1	A dog bit me while I was walking to work.	Yes	(No)
2	I hurt myself while I was washing my car.	(Yes)	No
3	My son broke his arm while he was skiing.	Yes	No
4	We exhausted ourselves while we were jogging.	Yes	No
5	My children hurt themselves while they were playing in the park.	Yes	No
6	My husband and I cut ourselves while we were slicing vegetables.	Yes	No
7	Barbie poked herself in the eye while she was putting on make-up.	Yes	No
8	I got a headache while I was doing my English homework.	Yes	No

FINISH THE LINES!

Complete the sentences with the correct verb and a reflexive pronoun.

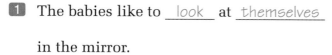

| clean | get dressed | study | teach | enjoy | look | talk | turn |

1 The babies like to __look__ at __themselves__

in the mirror.

2 Mrs. Jones is lonely. She always

_____ to _____.

3 This little boy can _____

by _____.

4 My roommate and I hate to _____

our apartment by _____.

5 I like to _____ English

by _____.

6 This lamp _____ on by _____

every night.

7 Marjorie wants to _____

_____ to play the piano.

8 You and your husband always seem

to _____ _____

at parties.

SEGMENT 44 SCRIPT ••

44.1 BY THEMSELVES (24:16)

CO-WORKER 1: What did you do yesterday?

CO-WORKER 2: I went to the beach.

CO-WORKER 1: Oh. Who did you go to the beach with?

CO-WORKER 2: Nobody. I went to the beach by myself.

CO-WORKER 1: You went by yourself?

CO-WORKER 2: Yes. I had a great time.

CO-WORKER 1: Hmm.

FRIEND 1: What did John do yesterday?

FRIEND 2: He went to the movies.

FRIEND 1: Oh. Who did he go to the movies with?

FRIEND 2: Nobody. He went to the movies by himself.

FRIEND 3: What did Tina do yesterday?

FRIEND 4: She played cards.

FRIEND 3: Oh. Who did she play cards with?

FRIEND 4: Nobody. She played cards by herself.

44.2 THEY'RE PAINTING THEIR HOUSE BY THEMSELVES (24:57)

HUSBAND 1: Look, Sheila! The Robinsons are painting their house by themselves!

WIFE 1: Hi, Lois. Hi, Larry. Are you guys really painting your house by yourselves?

WIFE 2: Yes, we are. We're painting it ourselves.

HUSBAND 1: It's going to look great!

HUSBAND 2: Thanks.

HUSBAND 1: What's that for, Larry?

HUSBAND 2: This? It sprays the paint on the house. It's really great. It almost paints the house by itself.

WIFE 1: Well, folks, it looks terrific. We'll see you later.

WIFE 2: Take care.

HUSBAND 2: Bye.

WIFE 1: You know . . . we should paint our house soon.

HUSBAND 1: By ourselves?

WIFE 1: Why not? They're doing it themselves!

HUSBAND 1: All right. We'll see.

44.3 THEY HAD A BAD DAY TODAY
(25:45)

ROOMMATE 1: You look upset.
ROOMMATE 2: I had a bad day today.
ROOMMATE 1: Why? What happened?
ROOMMATE 2: I lost my wallet while I was jogging through the park.
ROOMMATE 1: I'm sorry to hear that.

CO-WORKER 1: Harry looks upset.
CO-WORKER 2: He had a bad day today.
CO-WORKER 1: Why? What happened?
CO-WORKER 2: He cut himself while he was shaving.
CO-WORKER 1: What a shame!

44.4 THE REFLEXIVE INJURY CLINIC
(26:20)

MAN 1: What did you do?
MAN 2: Oh, I burned myself while I was cooking dinner.
MAN 1: Ooh!
MAN 2: How about you?
MAN 1: I hurt myself while I was bowling.
MAN 2: Your back?

MAN 1: Yeah . . . my back.
MAN 2: That's too bad.

WOMAN 1: What's the matter with your husband?
WOMAN 2: He poked himself in the eye.
WOMAN 1: Ouch! I bet that hurts!
MAN 3: It sure does!
WOMAN 2: What happened to your daughter?
WOMAN 1: She cut herself while she was slicing a bagel.
WOMAN 2: I'm sorry to hear that. Is this your first time here?
WOMAN 1: Oh, no. We come to this clinic all the time, whenever we hurt ourselves.

RECEPTIONIST: Reflexive Injury Clinic. Uh-húh. Uh-húh. It's broken? I see. And did you do this to yourself, or did it just happen? I see. Well, I'm sorry. I'm afraid we can't help you. We only take care of REFLEXIVE injuries. That's right. Things people do to themselves, like when they cut themselves, burn themselves, or hurt themselves. I'm sorry to hear it's broken, but I'm afraid we can't help you. Well, take care of yourself! Good-bye.

(To herself.)

My goodness!
WOMAN 1: Was he angry?
RECEPTIONIST: Oh, yes! He was beside himself!

(The phone rings again.)

RECEPTIONIST: Reflexive Injury Clinic. You cut yourself? That's too bad. Can you come in at two o'clock? See you then.

GRAMMAR

Reflexive Pronouns

I You He She It We You They	went by	myself. yourself. himself. herself. itself. ourselves. yourselves. themselves.

While-Clauses

I lost my wallet **while I was jogging through the park.**
He cut himself **while he was shaving.**

FUNCTIONS

Asking for and Reporting Information

What did you do yesterday?
  I *went to the beach.*

Who did you go *to the beach* with?
  I went *to the beach* by myself.

What's that for?
  It *sprays the paint on the house.*

I had a bad day today.
  Why? What happened?

I *lost my wallet* while I was *jogging through the park.*

What's the matter with *your husband?*
  He poked himself in the eye.

How about you?

Requesting

Can you come in at *two o'clock?*

Initiating a Topic

You look upset.

Complimenting

It's going to look great!

It looks terrific, *folks.*

Leave Taking

We'll see you later.

Take care of yourself.

Good-bye

Sympathizing

I'm sorry to hear that.

What a shame!

That's too bad.

Ouch! I bet that hurts!

I'm sorry. I'm afraid we can't help you.

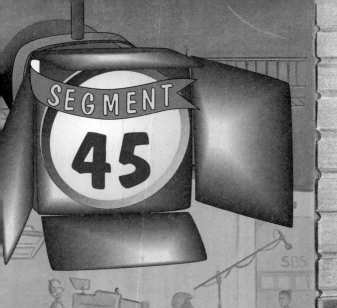

SEGMENT 45

- Be Able to
- Too + Adjective
- Ability
- Obligation

"She couldn't work; it was too late. She wasn't able to concentrate . . . Side by Side."

LESSON MENU

SBS-TV Backstage Bulletin Board

TO: Production Crew
Sets and props for this segment:

Backyard
basketball

Talk Show
microphone
chairs

Wedding
wedding gown
tuxedo

Classroom
desks

TO: Cast Members
Key words in this segment:

short
tired
nervous
shy
heavy
spicy
difficult

advice

stomachache

take care of

45.1 THEY COULDN'T (28:48)

A. (Could) / Would ^1 Peter play / pray ^2 on the baseball / basketball ^3 team

when he was a small / little ^4 boy?

B. No, he couldn't / wouldn't ^5. He was too short / smart ^6.

A. Could / Would ^7 Janet begin / finish ^8 her homework / housework ^9

last night?

B. No, she couldn't / wouldn't ^10. She was too tired / busy ^11.

A. Could / Would ^12 Stuart and Gloria meet / eat ^13 at

their wedding / meeting ^14?

B. No, they couldn't / wouldn't ^15. They were too jealous / nervous ^16.

FINISH THE SCRIPT!

Complete the following any way you wish.

> A. I couldn't .... because ....
>
> B. You couldn't? That's too bad.

45.2 THE OLIVIA WINFIELD SHOW (29:14)

SCENE CHECK

1 Olivia Winfield is a ____.

   a. talk show host

   b. game show host

2 Wayne McClaine is her ____.

   a. guest

   b. doctor

3 His book is called ____.

   a. *Never Say Couldn't*

   b. *Never Say Wouldn't*

4 He wrote it because he wanted to ____.

   a. make money

   b. help people

---

5 Millie and Timothy are Dr. McClaine's ____.

   a. patients

   b. friends

6 Timothy went to Dr. McClaine because he was ____.

   a. very shy

   b. a very nice guy

7 He couldn't ____.

   a. go to meetings

   b. go to parties

8 Millie went to Dr. McClaine because she was ____.

   a. tired

   b. nervous

9 She couldn't ____.

   a. fly in an airplane

   b. ride in an elevator

10 Dr. McClaine told her ____.

   a. she couldn't

   b. "Never say couldn't"

11 A woman in the audience wants to ask her boss for a ____.

   a. vacation

   b. raise

12 A man in the audience wants to ask a friend in the office to ____.

   a. go out

   b. quit

The video editor made a mistake! Put the following lines in the correct order.

1 ____ I was very shy.

__1__ Tell me, Timothy, why did you go to Dr. McClaine?

____ VERY shy.

____ How shy were you?

2 ____ That's right.

____ And that helped you?

____ And how did Dr. McClaine help you?

____ Never say couldn't.

____ He said, "Never say couldn't."

____ Absolutely. Now I'm not nervous at all.

3 ____ It's called *Yes, You Can.*

____ Oh, yes. My new book will be in the bookstores next month.

____ I couldn't say "No."

____ We have just a moment. Tell us about your new book.

____ I can't wait to see it. Thank you very much for being on our show today.

____ And the title?

THE NEXT LINE

Circle the correct response.

1 Welcome, Dr. McClaine.

a. You're welcome, Olivia.

b. Thank you, Olivia.

2 So you decided to write this book to help people?

a. Yes, I did.

b. Yes, you did.

3 Tell me, Timothy, why did you go to Dr. McClaine?

a. I would always cry.

b. I was very shy.

4 And what else did he do?

a. That was it.

b. What was it?

5 Why did you go see Dr. McClaine?

a. I was very allergic.

b. I was very nervous.

6 And that helped you?

a. Absolutely.

b. "Never say couldn't."

7 You really helped these people.

a. I have a lot of patience, Olivia.

b. I care about my patients, Olivia.

8 Do you have any advice?

a. Yes. "Never say couldn't."

b. "No, I couldn't."

A. Hi, Bob. It's Bill,

B. Oh hi, Bill. What's new?

A. Well, I just watched today's *Olivia Winfield Show,* and it was really fascinating!

B. Who was on today's show?

A. A doctor named Wayne McClaine. He just wrote a new book called,

_____ Never Say Couldn't _____ [1], and the book changed a lot of people's lives.

B. Really? How?

A. I'll tell you. A man named Timothy Tucker was very _____ [2]. He _____ [3] to people on the telephone.

He _____ [4] to parties. And he

_____ [5] at meetings at work. Also, a woman named Millie Franklin went to see Dr. McClaine. She was very

_____ [6]. She _____ [7] in an

airplane. She _____ [8] in traffic. And she

_____ [9] even _____ [10] the bus.

B. Boy! They were shy! How did Dr. McClaine help them?

A. Dr. McClaine told them, "_____ [11],"

B. What else did he do?

A. That was it. That's all he said.

B. And that helped?

A. It sure did. And listen to this: A woman from the studio audience told Dr. McClaine about her problem. She wanted to ask her boss for a raise, but she _____ [12].

She was too _____ [13]. Also, a man from the audience wanted to ask a

person from his office to go out on a date with him, but he was too _____ [14].

B. Did Dr. McClaine help these people?

A. Yes, he did.

B. Let me guess! He told them, "_____ [15],"

A. That's exactly what he did!

You're a surprise guest on "The Olivia Winfield Show!" Complete the scene any way you wish and then practice it with a friend.

OLIVIA: Tell our audience, why did you first go to see Dr. McClaine?

YOU: I went to him because I was very ....

I couldn't ....

I couldn't ....

I couldn't even ....!

OLIVIA: And how did Dr. McClaine help you?

YOU: He said, "..." And now ....

....!

OLIVIA: Thank you for your inspiring story.

WHAT DO YOU THINK?

Is Dr. McClaine a good doctor? ....

Do you think Dr. McClaine really helps people? ....

Does Olivia believe what Dr. McClaine is saying? ....

Do you believe him? Why or why not? ....

CLOSE-UP

Are there talk shows like "The Olivia Winfield Show" in your country? Describe them.

....

....

....

....

45.3 THEY WEREN'T ABLE TO (34:25)

SOUND CHECK

was	were	wasn't	weren't	able to	heavy	spicy	difficult

A. ___Was___ ¹ Jimmy ___able to___ ² lift his grandmother's suitcase?

B. No, he _____ ³. It was too _____ ⁴.

A. _____ ⁵ Patty _____ ⁶ finish the nachos she ordered last night?

B. No, she _____ ⁷. They were too _____ ⁸.

A. _____ ⁹ you _____ ¹⁰ solve the math problem?

B. No, we _____ ¹¹. It was too _____ ¹².

YES OR NO?

1	Jimmy could lift his grandmother's suitcase.	Yes	(No)
2	The suitcase was light.	Yes	No
3	The suitcase was too heavy.	Yes	No
4	Patty couldn't finish her nachos.	Yes	No
5	The nachos were spicy.	Yes	No
6	The students could solve the math problem.	Yes	No
7	It was an easy math problem.	Yes	No

WHAT'S THE WORD?

was	wasn't	were	weren't

1 My brother ___wasn't___ able to lift the box because it was too heavy.

2 I _____ able to eat the chili for lunch because it wasn't too spicy.

3 We _____ able to finish the puzzles because they were too difficult.

4 Susan and Max _____ able to come to the party because they didn't go away for the weekend.

5 It's too bad you _____ able to go to the movie. It _____ great!

45.4 THEY HAD TO (35:04)

SOUND CHECK

| wasn't | weren't | able to | had to | couldn't | enjoy |

A. Did Barbara _____ enjoy _____ ¹ herself at the concert last night?

B. Unfortunately, she _____ ² go to the concert last night. She _____ ³ study for an examination.

A. Did Mr. and Mrs. Wilson _____ ⁴ themselves at the symphony yesterday evening?

B. Unfortunately, they _____ ⁵ go to the symphony. They _____ ⁶ stay home and wait for the plumber.

WHAT HAPPENED?

1 Barbara _____ go to the concert last night.

  a. could

  (b.) couldn't

2 She _____ study for an exam.

  a. had to

  b. wanted to

3 She was probably _____.

  a. happy

  b. unhappy

4 Mr. and Mrs. Wilson _____ go to the symphony last night.

  a. were able to

  b. weren't able to

5 They _____ stay home and wait for the plumber.

  a. should

  b. had to

6 They probably had problems in their _____.

  a. kitchen

  b. living room

HOW ABOUT YOU?

Tell about some things you had to do last week.

....

....

45.5 MRS. MURPHY'S STUDENTS COULDN'T DO THEIR HOMEWORK (35:28)

DO YOU REMEMBER?

Mrs. Murphy's students didn't do their homework. Watch the scene and then see if you can remember each student's excuse.

1 Bob had a _____ last night.

   a. stomachache

   b. headache

2 Sally had to _____.

   a. go to the store

   b. go to the doctor

3 John had to _____.

   a. visit a friend in the hospital

   b. visit his grandmother in the hospital

4 Donna had to _____.

   a. take care of her mother

   b. take care of her baby sister

5 _____ in Richard's neighborhood.

   a. Everybody went out

   b. The lights went out

WHAT'S YOUR OPINION?

In your opinion, what are some good excuses for not doing your homework, for missing a meeting, or for being late for an appointment? What are some bad excuses?

Good Excuses	**Bad Excuses**
....	....
....	....
....	....
....	....

MATCH!

Choose the best excuse to complete each statement.

_e_ **1** I wasn't able to fix my door ____.

____ **2** I couldn't watch TV ____.

____ **3** I had to go to the hospital ____.

____ **4** I was able to go to the concert ____.

____ **5** I couldn't see you very well ____.

____ **6** I couldn't send you a letter ____.

____ **7** I had to lose weight ____.

____ **8** I was able to eat the whole pizza ____.

____ **9** I couldn't do my homework ____.

____ **10** I couldn't drive to New York ____.

____ **11** I wasn't able to wake up on time ____.

____ **12** I had to clean the house ____.

a. because I was too heavy

b. because I didn't have my glasses on

c. because my friends were coming to visit me

d. because it was broken

e. because I didn't have a hammer

f. because my car didn't work

g. because I was very hungry

h. because my alarm clock wasn't working

i. because I broke my leg

j. because I didn't have your address

k. because I didn't get the assignment

l. because I had some tickets

THE RIGHT WORD

1 They were upset because they (weren't / couldn't) able to go to the game.

2 I (could / able to) do the math problem.

3 I (had / had to) study all weekend.

4 I (was able / could) to leave work early.

5 We (had to / weren't) able to go to the movie because it was sold out.

6 Mr. and Mrs. Gomez (could / couldn't) go to work because they were sick.

7 Marie (had / had to) a headache because she listened to loud music all day.

8 We (weren't able / couldn't) open the window because it was stuck.

9 My friends (had to / weren't) go home early and study.

45.1 THEY COULDN'T (28:48)

FRIEND 1: Could Peter play on the basketball team when he was a little boy?

FRIEND 2: No, he couldn't. He was too short.

FATHER: Could Janet finish her homework last night?

MOTHER: No, she couldn't. She was too tired.

FRIEND 3: Could Stuart and Gloria eat at their wedding?

FRIEND 4: No, they couldn't. They were too nervous.

45.2 THE OLIVIA WINFIELD SHOW (29:14)

ANNOUNCER: Timothy couldn't talk to people on the telephone, and Millie couldn't fly in an airplane. Then they read this man's book, and it changed their lives.

OLIVIA: What do you do when you're too shy and too nervous? We'll meet a doctor who knows the answer, and we'll meet the people that he helped. All on today's *Olivia Winfield Show.*

Please welcome our guest for today's show, the author of the best-seller *Never Say Couldn't,* Dr. Wayne McClaine. Welcome, Dr. McClaine.

WAYNE: Thank you, Olivia. I'm glad to be here. And please . . . call me Wayne.

OLIVIA: Wayne, your new book is very popular. Tell us, why did you write it?

WAYNE: Well, Olivia, I'll tell you. In my office every day, I see people who say, "I couldn't do this," "I couldn't do that." And I always tell them, "Never say couldn't."

OLIVIA: So you decided to write this book to help people?

WAYNE: Yes, I did.

OLIVIA: Well, we'll meet the people that he helped. We have with us today two former patients of Dr. McClaine: Timothy Tucker and Millie Franklin. Tell me, Timothy, why did you go to Dr. McClaine?

TIMOTHY: I was very shy.

OLIVIA: How shy were you?

TIMOTHY: VERY shy. I couldn't talk to people on the telephone. I couldn't go to parties. I couldn't speak at meetings at work. Believe me, I was VERY shy.

OLIVIA: And how did Dr. McClaine help you?

TIMOTHY: He said, "Never say couldn't."

OLIVIA: And what else did he do?

TIMOTHY: That was it. He just said, "Never say couldn't."

OLIVIA: Oh. I see. And you, Millie? Why did you first go see Dr. McClaine?

MILLIE: I was very nervous. I couldn't fly in an airplane. I couldn't drive in traffic. I couldn't even take the bus.

OLIVIA: And how did Dr. McClaine help you?

MILLIE: He said, "Never say couldn't."

OLIVIA: Never say couldn't.

MILLIE: That's right.

OLIVIA: And that helped you?

MILLIE: Absolutely. Now I'm not nervous at all.

TIMOTHY: And I'm not a shy guy anymore.

OLIVIA: You're a wonderful person, Dr. McClaine. You really helped these people.

WAYNE: I care about my patients, Olivia. I really do.

OLIVIA: We have time for one or two questions from our studio audience. Yes.

WOMAN: Dr. McClaine? I want to ask my boss for a raise, but I'm afraid to. I tried to ask her for a raise last week, but I couldn't. I was too scared. Do you have any advice?

WAYNE: Yes. Never say couldn't.

WOMAN: Thank you, Dr. McClaine. I'll take your advice.

OLIVIA: And we have time for one more question. Go ahead.

MAN: Dr. McClaine. There's a very nice person at my office. I'd like to ask her to go out on a date with me. I almost asked her last week, but I couldn't. I was too nervous. What should I do?

WAYNE: Never say couldn't.

MAN: Thank you, Doctor. That's good advice.

OLIVIA: We have just a moment. Tell us about your new book.

WAYNE: Oh, yes. My new book will be in the bookstores next month.

OLIVIA: And the title?

WAYNE: It's called *Yes, You Can.*

OLIVIA: I can't wait to see it. Thank you very much for being on our show today.

WAYNE: I couldn't say "No."

OLIVIA: That's all the time we have for today's show. On our next show: people and their pets. What happens when husbands and wives don't agree about dogs and cats? See you next time.

ANNOUNCER: The *Olivia Winfield Show* is a production of Side by Side TV. Olivia Winfield's wardrobe by Clyde's Clothing. Taped before a live studio audience.

45.3 THEY WEREN'T ABLE TO (34:25)

PERSON 1: Was Jimmy able to lift his grandmother's suitcase?

PERSON 2: No, he wasn't able to. It was too heavy.

PERSON 3: Was Patty able to finish the nachos she ordered last night?

PERSON 4: No, she wasn't able to. They were too spicy.

TEACHER: Were you able to solve the math problem?

STUDENT: No, we weren't able to. It was too difficult.

45.4 THEY HAD TO (35:04)

FRIEND 1: Did Barbara enjoy herself at the concert last night?

FRIEND 2: Unfortunately, she wasn't able to go to the concert last night. She had to study for an examination.

PERSON 1: Did Mr. and Mrs. Wilson enjoy themselves at the symphony yesterday evening?

PERSON 2: Unfortunately, they couldn't go to the symphony. They had to stay home and wait for the plumber.

45.5 MRS. MURPHY'S STUDENTS COULDN'T DO THEIR HOMEWORK (35:28)

MRS. MURPHY: Okay, class. I'll collect your homework now. Bob? Where's your homework?

BOB: I'm sorry, Mrs. Murphy. I couldn't do it. I had a stomachache last night.

MRS. MURPHY: I see. Sally? Where's yours?

SALLY: I'm afraid I wasn't able to do it.

MRS. MURPHY: You weren't able to do it?

SALLY: No. I had to go to the doctor.

MRS. MURPHY: I see. John? Do you have yours?

JOHN: Sorry, Mrs. Murphy, I don't. I couldn't do my homework because I had to visit my grandmother in the hospital.

MRS. MURPHY: Oh. Donna?

DONNA: Mrs. Murphy, I'm really sorry. I had to take care of my baby sister while my mother worked late at the office.

MRS. MURPHY: I see. How about you, Richard?

RICHARD: Uh . . . Sorry. There was a blackout in my neighborhood last night.

MRS. MURPHY: Well, class, I hope you'll be able to do your homework tonight.

BOB: I promise.

SALLY: I will.

JOHN: Yes, Mrs. Murphy.

DONNA: Okay, Mrs. Murphy.

RICHARD: We all promise, Mrs. Murphy.

MRS. MURPHY: I certainly hope so.

GRAMMAR

Could

Could	I he she it we you they	play basketball?

Yes,	I he she it we you they	could.
No,		couldn't.

Had to

I He She It We You They	had to work.

Be Able to

Was	I he she it	able to go?
Were	we you they	

No,	I he she it	wasn't	able to.
	we you they	weren't	

FUNCTIONS

Inquiring about Ability

Could Janet *finish her homework last night?*
Was Jimmy able to *lift his grandmother's suitcase?*

Expressing Inability

No, *she* couldn't.
No, *he* wasn't able to.

I couldn't do it.

Describing

She was too *tired/short/ nervous . . .*

Inquiring about Satisfaction

Did you enjoy yourself *at the concert last night?*

Expressing Obligation

She had to *study for an examination.*

Expressing Regret

I'm afraid *I wasn't able to do it.*

Promising

I promise.

SEGMENT 46

- Have Got to
- Making Excuses

"I've got to work; she's got to, too. We won't be able to go with you . . . Side by Side."

LESSON MENU

SBS-TV Backstage Bulletin Board

TO: Production Crew
Sets and props for this segment:

Kitchen
apron
counter
knife
stove
telephone

Plumber's Office
telephone
wrench
table
chair

Apartments
boxes
telephone

Living Room
chair

TO: Cast Members
Key words in this segment:

be able to
have/has got to

broken pipe
fix

dog show
soccer coach

46.1 RING! RING! (37:08)

YES OR NO?

1	Michael Rivera wants Ted to come to a parents' meeting at school.	(Yes)	No
2	Michael Rivera is from the PTA.	Yes	No
3	Ted will be able to go to the meeting.	Yes	No
4	Michael Rivera says he'll take care of Ted Sanders' kids.	Yes	No
5	Judy calls and asks for Linda.	Yes	No
6	Judy forgot Linda is out of town this week.	Yes	No
7	Judy invites Ted and Linda to dinner on Saturday.	Yes	No
8	Ted and Linda will be able to go.	Yes	No
9	They've got to take their dog to a dog show.	Yes	No
10	Billy calls because he wants Alex to come over and do homework with him.	Yes	No
11	Alex has to do his homework.	Yes	No
12	Debbie Dawson calls Ted about Katie's baseball game.	Yes	No
13	Debbie is Katie's coach.	Yes	No
14	There's a game on Saturday afternoon.	Yes	No
15	Katie won't be able to go because it's her birthday.	Yes	No
16	Ted tells the coach that Katie won't be able to play in the game.	Yes	No
17	Ted baked the cake for too short a time.	Yes	No
18	The cake's got to bake for thirty minutes.	Yes	No
19	Ted baked the cake for twenty minutes.	Yes	No

The video editor made a mistake! Put the following lines in the correct order.

_____ Will Alex be able to come over and play after dinner?

_____ Oh hi, Billy.

_____ Bye, Billy.

_____ No, I'm afraid he won't. He's got to do his homework.

_____ Hello, Mr. Sanders. This is Billy.

_____ Oh, okay. Thanks, Mr. Sanders. Good-bye.

__1__ Hello.

THE NEXT LINE

Circle the correct response according to the video.

1 I've got to stay home and take care of the kids.

   a. I understand. Thanks anyway.

   b. Hello, Mr. Rivera.

2 She's on a business trip.

   a. Is Linda there?

   b. Oh, that's right. I forgot.

3 We've got to take Daisy to a dog show.

   a. You've got to WHAT?

   b. I'm afraid we won't be able to.

4 Some other time, okay?

   a. I won't be able to.

   b. Sure. We'd love to.

5 Say "hi" to Linda for me.

   a. I will.

   b. Hello.

6 He's got to do his homework.

   a. I'm afraid he won't.

   b. Oh, okay.

WHO IS EVERYBODY?

_c_ **1** Ted Sanders is _____.

_____ **2** Michael Rivera is _____.

_____ **3** Judy and Herman are _____.

_____ **4** Daisy is _____.

_____ **5** Billy is _____.

_____ **6** Debbie Dawson is _____.

a. Alex's friend

b. Linda and Ted's friends

c. Linda's husband

d. Linda and Ted's dog

e. Katie's soccer coach

f. a parent from the school

WHOSE LINE?

Choose the letter of the correct person for each line.

A **B** **C** **D**

_C_ **1** "Will Alex be able to come over and play after dinner?"

____ **2** "Will you be able to come to the parents' meeting at school tomorrow night?"

____ **3** "Is Linda there?"

____ **4** "Herman! Listen to this! They've got to take their dog to a dog show!"

____ **5** "Listen . . . will Katie be able to play in the soccer game this Saturday afternoon?"

____ **6** "I understand. Thanks anyway."

____ **7** "Oh, okay. Thanks, Mr. Sanders. Good-bye."

____ **8** "That's too bad. It's a very important game."

____ **9** "Well, sorry you can't come over this weekend. Some other time, okay?"

FUNCTION CHECK

Circle the word that tells what each person is expressing.

1 "Will you be able to come to the parents' meeting at school tomorrow night?" (a.) ability b. regret

2 "I won't be able to." a. inability b. inviting

3 "We've got to take Daisy to a dog show." a. inability b. obligation

4 "You've got to WHAT?" a. regret b. disbelief

5 "Sorry you can't come over this weekend." a. obligation b. regret

6 "Will Alex be able to come over and play after dinner?" a. ability b. disbelief

7 "No, I'm afraid he won't." a. regret b. obligation

8 "He's got to do his homework." a. regret b. obligation

9 "That's too bad. It's a very important game." a. regret b. inability

10 "I can't believe this!" a. regret b. disbelief

Put a circle around the correct answer.

1 "Will you be able to come to the parents' meeting at school tomorrow night?"

   a. Do you want to come to the meeting?

   (b.) Can you come to the meeting?

2 "I'm sorry. I won't be able to. My wife is on a business trip this week."

   a. My wife's company sent her on vacation.

   b. My wife is working away from home this week.

3 "Will Alex be able to come over and play after dinner?"

   a. Should Alex come over and play after dinner?

   b. Can Alex come over and play after dinner?

4 "I'm afraid he won't. He's got to do his homework."

   a. I'm sorry, but he can't come because he has to do his homework.

   b. I'm afraid he won't be able to do his homework.

5 "Linda is out of town this week."

   a. Linda is visiting the countryside this week.

   b. Linda isn't at home this week.

6 They can't come to dinner Saturday because they've got to take their dog to a dog show.

   a. They're going to take their dog to a dog show.

   b. They can't take their dog to a dog show.

7 Katie won't be able to play soccer. She's got to go to a birthday party.

   a. Katie wasn't at the soccer game because she was at a party.

   b. Katie won't be at the soccer game because she'll be at a party.

8 "That's too bad. It's a very important game."

   a. It's bad that it's an important game.

   b. I'm disappointed she has to go to a party and can't play soccer.

1 Ted Sanders sometimes sings while he makes dinner.   (Yes)   No

2 The phone is over the refrigerator.   Yes   No

3 He's cutting up carrots and tomatoes.   Yes   No

4 He's wearing a big white apron.   Yes   No

5 He hears the cake burning.   Yes   No

6 His daughter's name is Katie, and his son's name is Billy.   Yes   No

7 His dog's name is Daisy.   Yes   No

8 The phone rang six times.   Yes   No

46.2 I'M AFRAID I WON'T BE ABLE TO HELP YOU (40:41)

EDITING MIX-UP

The video editor made a mistake! Put the following lines in the correct order.

_____ I've got to take my son to the doctor.

_____ You won't? Why not?

__1__ I'm afraid I won't be able to help you move to your new apartment tomorrow.

_____ Don't worry about it! I'm sure I'll be able to move to my new apartment by myself.

MORE EXCUSES

Complete the excuses.

able to	won't be able to	have/has got to

1 I'm sorry I _____ won't be able to _____ come to your party on Saturday.

_____ study for an exam. I'm

sure _____ go out next Saturday.

2 I'm afraid I _____ meet you for lunch this Wednesday.

_____ go to the dentist. I'm sure _____

meet you next Wednesday.

3 I'm afraid Sally and I _____ come to your picnic on

Saturday. _____ take our cat to a cat show.

4 I'm afraid Katie _____ come to school on Tuesday.

_____ go to the doctor. I'm sure

_____ come to school on Wednesday.

5 I'm afraid Grandpa _____ take his walk today.

_____ go to his friend's 80th birthday party.

I'm sure _____ take his walk tomorrow.

6 I'm afraid Mary and I _____ play tennis with you on

Saturday morning. _____ get to our wedding!

46.3 THE BATHROOM PIPE IS BROKEN (40:59)

1 The plumber's name is Patty. (Yes) No

2 Mrs. Wilson called the plumber yesterday. Yes No

3 Mrs. Wilson has a broken pipe in her kitchen. Yes No

4 Patty the Plumber remembered the broken pipe. Yes No

5 Patty didn't fix the pipe yesterday because her son was sick. Yes No

6 Patty can fix the pipe today. Yes No

7 She's got to fix the heating system at the high school today. Yes No

8 She says she'll be able to come tomorrow. Yes No

9 She won't be able to come tomorrow because tomorrow is Sunday. Yes No

10 Patty spends her time on Sunday with her children. Yes No

11 Patty is coming to fix the pipe on Monday. Yes No

EDITING MIX-UP

The video editor made a mistake! Put the following lines in the correct order.

_____ Oh, yes. I remember. You've got the broken pipe in your bathroom. Right?

__1__ Hello. Patty's Plumbing. This is Patty.

_____ Yes, that's right.

_____ Hello. This is Mrs. Wilson calling again. I called yesterday.

_____ Yes. Much better, thanks. How are you?

_____ Are you feeling better now?

_____ Today? No, I'm afraid not. I've got to fix the heating system at the high school.

_____ Sorry I wasn't able to get over there yesterday. I was sick.

_____ Fine . . . but our shower . . . can you come over and fix it today?

> **FINISH THE SONG!**

Listen to the song and fill in the missing rhyming words.

My friend Jim called the other __day__¹. He said, "Would you like to see a play _____²?"

I didn't really want to _____³, so this is how I told him _____⁴.

I'm afraid I won't be able _____⁵. I have a lot of things to _____⁶.

I've got to wash my clothes and clean my house today.

But thank you for the invitation. I want to express my appreciation.

I'm sure that we'll be able to see a _____⁷—another _____⁸.

My friend Bob called the other _____⁹. He said, "Would you like to

rollerskate _____¹⁰?"

I didn't really want to _____¹¹ so this is how I told him _____¹².

I'm afraid I won't be able _____¹³. I have a lot of things to _____¹⁴.

I've got to paint my house and bathe my cat today.

But thank you for the invitation. I want to express my appreciation.

I'm sure that we'll be able to rollerskate—another day.

I'm sure that we'll be able to.

I'm sure that we'll be able to.

> **HOW ABOUT YOU?**

What do you say when you turn down an invitation?

....

....

EVEN MORE EXCUSES!

Poor Bob! He can't get anyone to help him! What excuses do these people have?

> **able to   have/has got to**

The painter ___won't be able to___ [1] finish painting the garage this week because

he says the weather is cold and ___it's got to___ [2] be warmer. Maybe

_____ [3] finish next week. Alice, from the Ajax

Repair Shop, _____ [4] fix Bob's refrigerator

because _____ [5] fix the mayor's stove.

Maybe _____ [6] fix it tomorrow. Germaine,

the gardener, is out of town and he says _____ [7]

cut the grass this week. He says _____ [8] cut it next

week. And no one from the telephone company _____ [9]

come and repair the phone because the workers are on strike. Someone

_____ [10] come when the strike is over!

WHAT DO YOU SAY?

If you are invited somewhere and don't want to go, there are polite and impolite ways to refuse the invitation. Read the situations below and circle the polite response.

1 Would you like to go for a walk in the park with me?

   a. No, I don't want to.

   (b.) I'm afraid I won't be able to. I have other plans today.

2 Will you be able to come over for dinner tomorrow night?

   a. I'm sorry, I can't. I've got to work tomorrow night. But, thanks for inviting me.

   b. I don't want to. I want to watch a program on TV.

3 How about going to a movie tonight?

   a. Sorry, I can't. I've got to study. for an exam tomorrow.

   b. No way!

4 Let's go shopping today!

   a. Thanks for the invitation, but I'm busy today. I'll be able to go on Saturday.

   b. I hate to go shopping. Why don't you go by yourself?

46.1 RING! RING! (37:08)

TED SANDERS:	Hello.
MR. RIVERA:	Hello. Is this Mr. Sanders?
TED SANDERS:	Yes, it is.
MR. RIVERA:	Hi. This is Michael Rivera from the P.T.A. calling.
TED SANDERS:	Hello, Mr. Rivera.
MR. RIVERA:	Will you be able to come to the parents' meeting at school tomorrow night?
TED SANDERS:	I'm sorry. I won't be able to. My wife is on a business trip this week, and I've got to stay home and take care of the kids.
MR. RIVERA:	I understand. Thanks anyway.
TED SANDERS:	Good-bye.
MR. RIVERA:	Bye.
TED SANDERS:	Hello.
JUDY:	Hi, Ted. This is Judy. Is Linda there?
TED SANDERS:	No, Judy. Linda's out of town this week. She's on a business trip.
JUDY:	Oh, that's right. I forgot. Listen, Ted . . . Herman and I were wondering: Will you and Linda be able to come over for dinner this Saturday evening?
TED SANDERS:	Saturday evening? Hmm. No, I'm afraid we won't be able to. We've got to take Daisy to a dog show.
JUDY:	You've got to WHAT?
TED SANDERS:	We've got to take Daisy to a dog show.

(To her husband.)

JUDY:	Herman! Listen to this!

They've got to take their dog to a dog show!

(To Ted.)

Well, sorry you can't come over this weekend. Some other time, okay?

TED SANDERS:	Sure. We'd love to. Thanks for inviting us.
JUDY:	Say "hi" to Linda for me!
TED SANDERS:	I will. Good-bye.
JUDY:	Bye.
TED SANDERS:	Hello.
BILLY:	Hello, Mr. Sanders. This is Billy.
TED SANDERS:	Oh hi, Billy.
BILLY:	Will Alex be able to come over and play after dinner?
TED SANDERS:	No, I'm afraid he won't. He's got to do his homework.
BILLY:	Oh, okay. Thanks, Mr. Sanders. Good-bye.
TED SANDERS:	Bye, Billy. (Oh, boy!)
TED SANDERS:	Hello.
DEBBIE DAWSON:	Hello. Is this Mr. Sanders?
TED SANDERS:	Yes, it is.
DEBBIE DAWSON:	This is Debbie Dawson, Katie's soccer coach.
TED SANDERS:	Oh hi, Coach, how are you?
DEBBIE DAWSON:	Fine. Listen . . . will Katie be able to play in the soccer game this Saturday afternoon?
TED SANDERS:	No, I'm afraid she won't be able to. She's got to go to a birthday party.
DEBBIE DAWSON:	That's too bad. It's a very important game.
TED SANDERS:	I'm sorry. She won't be able to play this week.
DEBBIE DAWSON:	Well, okay. Thank you.
TED SANDERS:	Good-bye.

(Ted smells smoke.)

TED SANDERS:	Oh, no! The cake! I can't believe this! It's got to bake

for twenty minutes, and I
baked it for thirty! Oh, boy!

46.2   I'M AFRAID I WON'T BE ABLE TO HELP YOU (40:41)

NEIGHBOR 1: I'm afraid I won't be able to help you move to your new apartment tomorrow.
NEIGHBOR 2: You won't? Why not?
NEIGHBOR 1: I've got to take my son to the doctor.
NEIGHBOR 2: Don't worry about it! I'm sure I'll be able to move to my new apartment by myself.

46.3   THE BATHROOM PIPE IS BROKEN (40:59)

PATTY: Hello. Patty's Plumbing. This is Patty.
MRS. WILSON: Hello. This is Mrs. Wilson calling again. I called yesterday.
PATTY: Oh, yes. I remember. You've got the broken pipe in your bathroom. Right?
MRS. WILSON: Yes, that's right.
PATTY: Sorry I wasn't able to get over there yesterday. I was sick.
MRS. WILSON: Are you feeling better now?
PATTY: Yes. Much better, thanks. How are you?
MRS. WILSON: Fine . . . but our shower . . . can you come over and fix it today?
PATTY: Today? No, I'm afraid not. I've got to fix the heating system at the high school.
MRS. WILSON: I see. How about tomorrow?
PATTY: Tomorrow? I won't be able to come over tomorrow. Tomorrow's Sunday.
MRS. WILSON: I suppose you don't work on Sundays.
PATTY: No. It's my only day with my kids. How's Monday?
MRS. WILSON: I guess if it's got to be Monday, it's got to be Monday.
MR. WILSON: Monday?
PATTY: Yeah . . . I think it's got to be Monday. See you then.
MRS. WILSON: Good-bye.
MR. WILSON: Monday?
MRS. WILSON: Monday.

46.4   I'M AFRAID I WON'T BE ABLE TO—Music Video (42:17)

My friend Jim called the other day.
He said, "Would you like to see a play today?"
I didn't really want to go,
So this is how I told him no.

I'm afraid I won't be able to.
I have a lot of things to do.
I've got to wash my clothes
And clean my house today.

But thank you for the invitation.
I want to express my appreciation.
I'm sure that we'll be able to
See a play—another day.

My friend Bob called the other day.
He said, "Would you like to rollerskate today?"
I didn't really want to go,
So this is how I told him no.

I'm afraid I won't be able to.
I have a lot of things to do.
I've got to paint my house
And bathe my cat today.

But thank you for the invitation.
I want to express my appreciation.
I'm sure that we'll be able to
Rollerskate—another day.

I'm sure that we'll be able to.
I'm sure that we'll be able to.

GRAMMAR

Be Able to

I'll He'll She'll It'll We'll You'll They'll	**be able to** help you.

I He She It We You They	**won't be able to** help you.

Have Got to

I've We've You've They've He's She's It's	**got to** work.

FUNCTIONS

Inquiring about Ability

Will you be able to *come to the parents' meeting at school tomorrow night?*

Expressing Inability

I won't be able to.

Expressing Obligation

I've got to *stay home and take care of the kids.*

Expressing Disbelief

You've got to WHAT?!

Expressing Regret

Sorry *you can't come over this weekend.*

I'm afraid I won't be able to *help you move to your new apartment tomorrow.*

Sorry I wasn't able to *get over there yesterday.*

Describing

It's a very *important game.*

I was *sick.*

Expressing Certainty

I'm sure *I'll be able to move to my new apartment by myself.*

Remembering–Forgetting

I forgot.

I remember.

Making an Invitation

Would you like to *see a play today?*

Declining an Invitation

I'm afraid I won't be able to.

But thank you for the invitation.

I'm sure we'll be able to *see a play another day.*

SEGMENT 47

- Count/Non-Count Nouns
- Nutrition
- Medical Advice

"Fewer cookies on his plate. The doctor says he must lose weight . . . Side by Side."

LESSON MENU

SBS-TV Backstage Bulletin Board

TO: Production Crew
Sets and props for this segment:

Doctor's Office
desk
note pad

Kitchen
table

Living Room
sofa

TO: Cast Members
Key words in this segment:

more	bread	checkup
less	butter	diet
fewer	cookies	exercise
	desserts	fat
	dog biscuits	fatty
	fish	heavy
	margarine	lean
	meat	pounds
	potatoes	rich
	rice	vet
	skim milk	
	vegetables	
	whole milk	

47.1 HENRY'S DIET (44:34)

MORE, LESS, OR FEWER?

Put a check next to Henry's doctor's advice.

		more	less	fewer
1	bread	___	✓	___
2	cookies	___	___	___
3	fish	___	___	___
4	meat	___	___	___
5	vegetables	___	___	___
6	potatoes	___	___	___
7	butter	___	___	___
8	margarine	___	___	___
9	rich desserts	___	___	___

SCENE CHECK

1. Dr. Walker just ___ Henry.
   a. met
   b. examined ⟵
2. He thinks that in general Henry is ___.
   a. healthy
   b. unhealthy
3. The only thing he's worried about is Henry's ___.
   a. height
   b. weight
4. He thinks Henry should be ___.
   a. fatter
   b. thinner
5. Dr. Walker thinks that bread and cookies are ___.
   a. healthy
   b. fattening
6. He thinks that fish is ___ than meat.
   a. more expensive
   b. healthier

7. He thinks that Henry ___ eat more vegetables.
   a. must
   b. shouldn't
8. Dr. Walker thinks that butter ___ as healthy as margarine.
   a. is
   b. isn't
9. He thinks that Henry should ___ rich desserts.
   a. eat
   b. avoid
10. The doctor thinks the diet ___ help.
    a. will
    b. won't
11. He thinks that Henry should lose ___.
    a. approximately ten pounds
    b. more than ten pounds

47.2 SBS-TV ON LOCATION (45:40)

Before you watch the interview, see if you can predict what advice these people will give for losing weight. Then watch and see if your predictions were correct.

| more | fewer | less |

1 Eat _____less_____ fatty meat.

2 Eat _____ potatoes and _____ rice.

3 Eat _____ green vegetables.

4 Have _____ rich desserts.

5 Eat _____ lean meat.

6 Drink _____ whole milk.

7 _____ butter, _____ margarine.

What's this man's advice for staying healthy?

If you ask me, I think all this talk about ___diets___¹ is ridiculous! Eat _____²

of _____³, eat _____⁴ of _____⁵, eat _____⁶

of _____⁷ . . . it's crazy! I say, eat what you want, but not _____⁸.

And _____⁹! That's the most important thing! People don't

_____¹⁰ enough these days. Well, gotta go. Nice talking with you.

47.3 I MUST LOSE SOME WEIGHT (46:33)

must   mustn't   don't have to

I had my yearly checkup today. My doctor told me that I _____must_____ ¹ lose some weight. I _____² stop eating ice cream. But I _____³ eat as much ice cream as I did before.

THEY WENT TO THE DOCTOR TODAY

must   mustn't   don't have to

1 My doctor told me I _____must_____ stop eating rich foods.

2  My doctor is concerned. She says I _____ eat so much candy.

3 I went to the doctor, and he said I _____ stop eating bread, but I _____ eat as much bread as I do now.

4 My doctor thinks I eat too many desserts. She tells me that I _____ have any more desserts for the next six months!

5 According to my doctor, I _____ lose 25 pounds! He said, "You _____ stop eating completely, but you _____ eat very carefully."

6  My doctor says that I _____ exercise more. I _____ exercise very hard, but I _____ exercise every day!

47.4 FIFI'S ON A DIET (46:53)

EDITING MIX-UP

The video editor made a mistake! Put the following lines in the correct order.

_____ What did the vet say?

__1__ Fifi had her yearly checkup today. Didn't you, Fifi?

_____ I can't believe it! Our dog's on a diet!

_____ He said Fifi's a little too heavy, and she must lose some weight.

_____ No, she doesn't. But she mustn't eat as many dog biscuits as she did before.

_____ So Fifi's fat?

_____ Oh, really? Does she have to stop eating dog biscuits?

_____ Jeffrey! Don't say that word in front of Fifi! She's just got to lose a little weight, that's all.

ON CAMERA 1

You're a veterinarian who is appearing on Side by Side TV! Give some advice for dogs, like Fifi, who need to lose weight. What do you recommend?

....

....

....

....

....

ON CAMERA 2

You're a "people" doctor who is appearing on Side by Side TV! What are your recommendations for people who want to lose weight?

....

....

....

....

....

THE RIGHT WORD

1 Let's buy ⟨more / fewer⟩ green vegetables! Everybody knows they're good for your health.

2 Can't we get ⟨a few / fewer⟩ boxes of cookies, Mom? I know they aren't very healthy, but I LOVE them!

3 We need to eat ⟨more / less⟩ butter. The doctor says it isn't good for you.

4 I think we need ⟨more / few⟩ chicken. Everyone says it's better for you than red meat.

5 We ⟨must / mustn't⟩ eat too much ice cream. It's delicious . . . but very fattening!

6 We ⟨should / shouldn't⟩ buy potato chips any more! Popcorn is a much healthier snack food.

7 I ⟨don't have to / have to⟩ eat fewer rich desserts, but I ⟨don't have to / have to⟩ give them up completely.

8 ⟨Shouldn't / Should⟩ we buy fruit juice or soda? Which is healthier for you?

MY DENTIST SAYS . . .

What advice does your dentist give you?

_d_ **1** You must brush your teeth _____.

_____ **2** You should visit the dentist _____.

_____ **3** Don't forget to _____.

_____ **4** You shouldn't eat too much _____.

_____ **5** Remember! Your dentist is your _____.

a. every six months

b. friend

c. floss

d. after every meal

e. candy

47.1 HENRY'S DIET (44:34)

DR. WALKER: Well, Henry, everything looks okay except for one thing.

HENRY: What's that, Doctor Walker?

DR. WALKER: It's your weight. You're a little too heavy.

HENRY: I see.

DR. WALKER: I'm going to put you on this diet.

HENRY: Okay.

DR. WALKER: You must eat less bread, fewer cookies, more fish, and less meat. And you must eat more vegetables, but fewer potatoes, less butter, and more margarine. And you MUST eat fewer rich desserts.

HENRY: Fewer rich desserts?!

DR. WALKER: That's right, Henry. Sorry.

HENRY: I understand.

DR. WALKER: I think with this diet, Henry, you'll lose some weight, and that'll be very good for you.

HENRY: How many pounds should I lose?

DR. WALKER: Oh . . . maybe ten pounds, more or less.

HENRY: Well, thank you very much, Doctor Walker.

DR. WALKER: You're welcome, Henry. Good to see you again.

47.2 SBS-TV ON LOCATION (45:40)

INTERVIEWER: What's your advice for people who want to lose weight?

PERSON 1: Eat less fatty meat.

PERSON 2: Eat fewer potatoes and less rice.

PERSON 3: Eat more green vegetables.

PERSON 4: Have fewer rich desserts. Definitely stay away from those rich desserts.

PERSON 5: Eat more lean meat.

PERSON 6: Drink less whole milk. Have skim milk instead. It doesn't taste so bad after you get used to it.

PERSON 7: Less butter, more margarine. That's my advice.

PERSON 8: If you ask me, I think all this talk about diets is ridiculous! Eat fewer of these, eat less of this, eat more of that. . . it's crazy! I say, eat what you want, but not too much. And exercise! That's the most important thing! People don't exercise enough these days. Well, gotta go. Nice talking with you.

47.3 I MUST LOSE SOME WEIGHT (46:33)

WIFE: I had my yearly checkup today.

HUSBAND: What did the doctor say?

WIFE: She told me I'm a little too heavy, and I must lose some weight.

HUSBAND: Do you have to stop eating ice cream?

WIFE: No, but I mustn't eat as much ice cream as I did before.

47.4 FIFI'S ON A DIET! (46:53)

WIFE: Fifi had her yearly checkup today. Didn't you, Fifi?

HUSBAND: What did the vet say?

WIFE: He said Fifi's a little too heavy, and she must lose some weight.

HUSBAND: Oh, really? Does she have to stop eating dog biscuits?

WIFE: No, she doesn't. But she mustn't eat as many dog biscuits as she did before.

HUSBAND: So Fifi's fat?

WIFE: Jeffrey! Don't say that word in front of Fifi! She's just got to lose a little weight, that's all.

HUSBAND: I can't believe it! Our dog's on a diet!

GRAMMAR

Must

I He She It We You They	**must** lose weight.

I He She It We You They	**mustn't** eat ice cream.

Count/Non-Count Nouns

Non-Count

You must eat	more less	bread. fish. meat.

Count

You must eat	more fewer	cookies. potatoes. eggs.

FUNCTIONS

Expressing Understanding

I see.

Expressing Obligation

You must *eat less bread.*

I mustn't *eat as much ice cream as I did before.*

Confirming

That's right, *Henry.*

Expressing Gratitude

Thank you very much.

Giving Advice

Eat *more green vegetables.*

Leave Taking

Nice talking with you.

Asking for and Reporting Information

She told me *I'm a little too heavy.*

What did *the doctor* say?

Inquiring about Obligation

Do you have to *stop eating ice cream?*

SEGMENT 48

- **Must vs. Should**
- **Medical Advice**
- **Home Remedies**

"You should call me when it hurts. You must stop eating rich desserts . . . Side by Side."

SBS-TV Backstage Bulletin Board

TO: Production Crew
Sets and props for this segment:

Doctor's Office
- desk
- chairs
- Walkman
- headphones

TV Studio
- chair
- script
- glass
- paper bag

TO: Cast Members
Key words in this segment:

- should
- must

- worried about
- heart
- hearing

- advice
- cold
- fluids

- hiccups
- breathing
- scare

- sore throat

48.1 REALLY, DOCTOR? (47:44)

WHAT'S HAPPENING?

1 The doctor is _____ about Mr. Jones's heart.

a. concerned

b. optimistic

2 It's obvious that Mr. Jones _____ eat rich desserts.

a. doesn't like to

b. likes to

3 The doctor says that it's very _____ for Mr. Jones to watch what he eats.

a. nice

b. important

4 The doctor thinks Mr. Jones will have heart problems in the future if he _____ eating rich desserts.

a. stops

b. continues

OTHER PEOPLE'S PROBLEMS

What's the doctors' advice?

1 My doctor is concerned about my legs. She thinks I run too much. She says I must / ~~mustn't~~ run as much as I do.

2 My doctor says I'm going to have problems with my back in the future. That's why he says I must / mustn't stop lifting heavy things.

3 "You mustn't / should watch television so much! I'm afraid you're going to have to wear glasses soon!" That's what Dr. Williams said when I spoke with him yesterday.

4 My doctor is worried about my shoulder. She tells me I must / mustn't play tennis for a while. That's really too bad.

1. Nicholas is listening to the doctor.   Yes   **No**

2. The doctor is worried about Nicholas's earring.   Yes   No

3. The doctor takes the headphones off Nicholas's head.   Yes   No

4. The doctor says Nicholas has to stop listening to music.   Yes   No

5. Nicholas must stop listening to loud rock music with his headphones.   Yes   No

6. The doctor is afraid Nicholas will have serious problems with his heart some day.   Yes   No

7. Nicholas says he'll do whatever the doctor says.   Yes   No

8. Nicholas's favorite group is The Grateful Dead.   Yes   No

9. The doctor's favorite group is U2.   Yes   No

WHAT DOES IT MEAN?

1. "Well, Nicholas, I'm really worried about your hearing."

   a. He's worried Nicholas can hear too much.

   b. He's worried Nicholas can't hear very well.

2. "Now, Nicholas, we've got to talk about your hearing."

   a. The doctor wants Nicholas to listen to a talk about hearing.

   b. The doctor wants to discuss Nicholas's ability to hear.

3. "You MUST stop listening to loud rock music with those headphones."

   a. Nicholas should listen to loud classical music with his headphones.

   b. Nicholas shouldn't listen to loud music with his headphones because it's bad for his hearing.

4. "If you don't, you're going to have serious problems with your hearing some day."

   a. You won't be able to hear very well when you get older.

   b. You'll hear serious problems when you get older.

5. "By the way, what's your favorite group?"

   a. What's a favorite group?

   b. What group do you like the best?

SCRAMBLED SOUND TRACK

The sound track is all mixed up! Put the words in the correct order.

Excuse me. I have a bad cold. Do you have any advice?

1 | and | You | stay | in | rest. | should | bed

You should stay in bed and rest.

2 | water, | fluids: | You | juice, | drink | lots | whatever. | should | of

help. | That'll

3 | a | and | hot, | should | shower | the | You | nice | breathe | in

air. | take | hot | steamy

lot | You'll | a | better. | feel

4 | have | I | tea | When | a | drink | with | cold, | hot | lemon. | I

5 | soup. | Chicken | for | the | medicine | a | It's | best | cold.

me. | Believe | talking | I | about. | what | know | I'm

some | and | disappear, | Have | like | just | chicken | soup, | will | cold | your | that!

48.4 JENNIFER HAS THE HICCUPS! (49:55)

Jennifer has the hiccups and other Side by Side TV cast members are giving her advice. Circle the correct answers.

1 Jennifer _____ the hiccups.

   a. wants

   b. has

2 Maria has some _____ for Jennifer.

   a. dice

   b. advice

3 According to Maria, Jennifer should _____ breathing and count to ten.

   a. start

   b. stop

4 Jennifer _____ Maria's advice.

   a. takes

   b. doesn't take

5 Michael wants to know why Jennifer is _____ her breath.

   a. helping

   b. holding

6 According to Michael, that _____ work.

   a. will

   b. won't

7 Maria _____ with Michael.

   a. agrees

   b. disagrees

8 Maria's advice _____.

   a. didn't work

   b. worked

9 According to Michael, Jennifer should drink _____ water.

   a. a glass of

   b. a little

10 His _____ gave him that advice.

   a. mother

   b. grandmother

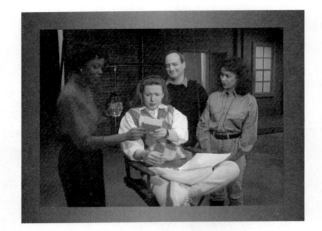

11 Gloria is _____ that Jennifer is drinking water.

   a. unhappy

   b. surprised

12 She thinks that's a _____ idea.

   a. good

   b. bad

13 Gloria gives Jennifer a _____.

   a. magazine

   b. paper bag

14 She tells her to _____.

   a. blow into it

   b. hold it

15 She learned that from her _____.

   a. mother and father

   b. grandmother and grandfather

16 David thinks that's a _____ idea.

   a. good

   b. bad

17 He thinks they should _____ Jennifer.

   a. scare

   b. stare at

18 He does this by saying _____

   a. "Ugh!"

   b. "Boo!"

19 Gloria thinks that was a _____ thing to do.

   a. wonderful

   b. terrible

20 David's advice _____.

   a. worked.

   b. didn't work.

MORE ADVICE

David has a sore throat, and the cast members give him advice. Match the lines.

__c__ **1** You should gargle with _____.

_____ **2** You should drink _____.

_____ **3** Have some warm _____.

_____ **4** You should take _____.

a. a hot shower

b. milk with honey

c. some warm salty water

d. hot tea with lemon

EDITING MIX-UP

The video editor made a mistake! Put the following lines in the correct order.

1

____ Okay.

____ Do you want some advice?

_1_ Hi, Jennifer.

____ Sure.

____ Hi, Maria.

____ You should stop breathing and count to ten.

____ Yes, I do.

____ Do you have the hiccups?

2

____ Well, that won't work.

____ Sure it will. It works for me all the time.

____ She's holding her breath. She has the hiccups.

____ What's Jennifer doing?

3

____ So why is she drinking water?

____ Hi, guys! What's up?

____ Because Michael's grandmother said so!

____ Jennifer's got the hiccups.

____ That's ridiculous! That won't help!

FINISH THE SENTENCE!

_d_ **1** What's ____?   a. ridiculous

____ **2** Do you want some ____?   b. on

____ **3** You should stop ____.   c. gone

____ **4** Count to ____.   d. up

____ **5** Take small ____.   e. paper bag

____ **6** That's ____!   f. will

____ **7** Blow into a ____.   g. breathing

____ **8** What's going ____?   h. sips

____ **9** Sure, it ____.   i. ten

____ **10** They're ____!   j. advice

HELP THESE PEOPLE!

Give advice to these people.

1 I have a toothache! Do you have any advice?

....
....
....
....

2 My nose is bleeding! What should I do?

....
....
....
....

3 I burned myself! Do you have any advice?

....
....
....
....

4 I have a stomachache! Do you have any advice?

....
....
....
....

ADVICE SURVEY

Ask three friends about their advice for one of the problems above. Do you agree or disagree with their advice?

Friend's Name	Advice	Do you agree or disagree?
Susan	If you burn yourself, you should put cold water on the burn.	I agree.
1.		
2.		
3.		

THE BEST RESPONSE

Choose the best response.

<u> c </u> **1** I'm really worried about your weight.

_____ **2** Should I exercise more?

_____ **3** What should my boyfriend do about his weight?

_____ **4** I have a headache. Do you have any advice?

_____ **5** That won't work!

_____ **6** Why is she drinking tea?

_____ **7** It's gone! My headache is gone!

a. Sure it will! It works all the time for me!

b. Yes. Take two aspirin and go to bed.

c. Do I eat too much?

d. See, I told you it would work!

e. He's got to eat fewer rich desserts.

f. Yes, you must. If you don't, you're going to have problems with your heart.

g. She's got a bad cold.

MUST OR SHOULD?

*Harry is going to France on vacation. Read the following statements and put an **S** next to the things he should do and an **M** next to the things he must do.*

<u> S </u> **1** Read a book about France.

_____ **2** Buy his airline ticket.

_____ **3** Get a passport.

_____ **4** Learn some French.

_____ **5** Pack his suitcase.

_____ **6** Get to the airport before the plane leaves.

_____ **7** Learn a little about French food.

_____ **8** Find out the time difference between his hometown and France.

_____ **9** Bring his friends' addresses, so he can send postcards home.

_____ **10** Find out if he needs to give tips in restaurants.

Do you have any more advice for Harry?

He should ....

He must ....

48.1   REALLY, DOCTOR?   (47:44)

DOCTOR: I'm really worried about your heart.

MR. JONES: Really, Doctor? Should I stop eating rich desserts?

DOCTOR: Mr. Jones! You MUST stop eating rich desserts! If you don't, you're going to have serious problems with your heart some day.

MR. JONES: I see.

48.2   I'M REALLY WORRIED ABOUT YOUR HEARING   (48:05)

DOCTOR: Well, Nicholas, I'm really worried about your hearing. Nicholas, I'm really worried about your hearing!

(The doctor removes the earphones Nicholas is wearing.)

DOCTOR: Now, Nicholas, we've got to talk about your hearing.

NICHOLAS: My WHAT?

DOCTOR: Your hearing.

NICHOLAS: Oh. Should I stop listening to music?

DOCTOR: Well, you don't have to stop listening to music, but you MUST stop listening to loud rock music with those headphones. If you don't, you're going to have serious problems with your hearing some day.

NICHOLAS: Okay. Whatever you say.

DOCTOR: Nice to see you again.

NICHOLAS: Nice to see you, too.

DOCTOR: Oh, Nicholas?

NICHOLAS: Yes?

DOCTOR: By the way, what's your favorite group?

NICHOLAS: U2. What's yours?

DOCTOR: The Grateful Dead.

NICHOLAS: Oh, cool! See ya, Doc!

DOCTOR: See ya, Nicholas!

48.3   SBS-TV ON LOCATION   (49:15)

INTERVIEWER: Excuse me. I have a bad cold. Do you have any advice?

PERSON 1:   Yes. You should stay in bed and rest.

PERSON 2:   You should drink lots of fluids: water, juice, whatever. That'll help.

PERSON 3:   You should take a nice hot shower and breathe in the hot, steamy air. You'll feel a lot better.

PERSON 4:   When I have a cold, I drink hot tea with lemon.

PERSON 5:   Chicken soup. It's the best medicine for a cold. Believe me. I know what I'm talking about. Have some chicken soup, and your cold will disappear, just like that!

48.4   JENNIFER HAS THE HICCUPS!

(49:55)

MARIA: Hi, Jennifer.

JENNIFER: Hi, Maria.

MARIA: Do you have the hiccups?

JENNIFER: Yes, I do.

MARIA: Do you want some advice?

JENNIFER: Sure.

MARIA: You should stop breathing and count to ten.

JENNIFER: Okay.

(Jennifer holds her breath. Michael comes by with a glass of water.)

MICHAEL: Hi, Jennifer. Hi, Maria. What's Jennifer doing?

MARIA: She's holding her breath. She has the hiccups.

MICHAEL: That won't work.

MARIA: Sure it will. It works for me all the time.

JENNIFER: Ten! Phew!

MARIA: Well?

(Jennifer hiccups.)

JENNIFER: Didn't work.

MICHAEL: See? I told you. Here, Jennifer. You should drink a little water. Just take small sips. I learned that from my grandmother.

JENNIFER: Thanks, Michael.

GLORIA: Hi, guys. What's up?

MICHAEL: Jennifer's got the hiccups.

GLORIA: So why is she drinking water?

MARIA: Because Michael's grandmother said so!

GLORIA: That's ridiculous! That won't help!

(Gloria gives Jennifer a brown paper bag.)

GLORIA: Jennifer, give me the glass, and take this.

JENNIFER: A paper bag? What should I do with THIS?

GLORIA: If you blow into the paper bag, your hiccups will stop. I learned that from my Mom and Dad when I was a little girl.

JENNIFER: Okay.

(Jennifer blows into the bag. David comes by.)

DAVID: What's going on?

GLORIA: Jennifer has the hiccups.

DAVID: Why is she blowing into that paper bag? THAT won't help.

GLORIA: Sure it will.

MICHAEL: No, it won't, Gloria.

MARIA: David? What do YOU think?

DAVID: I think we should scare her.

MARIA: Scare her?

DAVID: Yes. Watch.

(David scares Jennifer.)

DAVID: BOO!!!

(Jennifer gasps.)

DAVID: Sorry I scared you, Jennifer.

GLORIA: That was mean, David.

MARIA: Jennifer, are you okay?

JENNIFER: They're gone! The hiccups are gone!

DAVID: See? I told you.

JENNIFER: Thanks, David. But what's wrong with your voice?

DAVID: Oh, nothing. I just have a sore throat.

JENNIFER: You should gargle with some warm salty water.

MICHAEL: No, you shouldn't, David. You should drink hot tea with lemon.

GLORIA: David, don't listen to him. Have some warm milk with honey. That's what I do.

MARIA: In my opinion, you should take a hot shower. It'll really help.

GRAMMAR

Must

I He She It We You They	**must** stop eating rich desserts.

Should

I He She It We You They	**should** stay in bed and rest.

FUNCTIONS

Expressing Worry

I'm really worried about *your heart.*

Expressing Surprise

Really, *Doctor?*

Asking for Advice

Do you have any advice?

Should I *stop eating rich desserts?*

Offering Advice

You should *stay in bed and rest.*

Expressing Obligation

You must *stop eating rich desserts!*

Expressing Disagreement

That's ridiculous!

That won't *help at all!*

Apologizing

Sorry *I scared you.*

Greeting People

Hi, *Jennifer.*

What's up?

Leave Taking

Nice to see you again.
   Nice to see you, too.

See ya, *Nicholas.*

SEGMENT 49

- **Future Continuous Tense**
- **Time Expressions**
- **Future Activities**

"I'll be cooking; she'll be too. We'll be making lunch for you . . . Side by Side."

LESSON MENU

SBS-TV Backstage Bulletin Board

TO: Production Crew
Sets and props for this segment:

Living Room
- counter
- chair
- telephones
- sofa

TO: Cast Members
Key words in this segment:

play	get married
read	hear from
shop	take
stay	visit
study	work
watch	
write	

EDITING MIX-UP 1

The video editor made a mistake! Put the following lines in the correct order.

____ Pretty good.

__1_ Hi, Bob. This is Dad.

____ She's fine. So what's new with you?

____ That's good. I'm glad to hear that.

____ How's Mom?

____ Oh hi, Dad. How are you?

____ Nothing much. Everybody's okay here.

WHAT WILL EVERYBODY BE DOING?

study	stay	do	write	watch	play	read

FATHER: Will you be home this evening?

SON: Yes, I will. ___I'll be reading___ ¹.

FATHER: Oh. And how about Louise? Will she be home this evening?

SON: Yes, she will.

_____²

some letters.

FATHER: What _____³ Danny

_____⁴?

SON: _____⁵

for a big math test.

FATHER: And how about Julie and Laura?

SON: _____⁶ with their toys and

_____⁷ TV.

FATHER: Oh. That's nice. It sounds like you're all going to be very busy.

SON: Say, Dad, what _____⁸ you and Mom _____⁹ this evening?

FATHER: Oh, nothing much. I guess _____¹⁰ home.

SON: _____¹¹ home?

FATHER: Yes. I suppose so.

EDITING MIX-UP 2

The video editor made another mistake! Put the following lines in the correct order.

_____ Bye, Dad.

_____ How's 6:30?

_____ What's that, Bob?

_____ That sounds nice, Bob. Thank you.

_____ Bye.

_____ Can you and Mom come over for dinner this evening? We can have a nice dinner, and then you can play with the kids for a while.

__1__ Well, I have a great idea.

_____ 6:30? I'm sure that'll be fine. We'll see you then.

HOW ABOUT YOU?

Is there someone you should call? Tell about the people you usually talk to on the telephone. How often do you talk to them? What do you talk about?

....

....

....

....

THE RIGHT RESPONSE

__b__ **1** So what's new with you?

_____ **2** Everybody's okay here.

_____ **3** How are you?

_____ **4** You'll be staying home?

_____ **5** I have a great idea.

_____ **6** Bye.

a. I suppose so.

b. Nothing much.

c. Bye.

d. Pretty good.

e. That's good.

f. What's that?

49.2 HI, GLORIA. THIS IS ARTHUR. (54:08)

Circle the lines you hear.

1 a. Can I come over and see you this evening?

   (b.) Can I come over and visit this evening?

2 a. I'll be robbing the supermarket.

   b. I'll be shopping at the supermarket.

3 a. I'm afraid I won't be home tomorrow evening.

   b. I'm afraid to be alone tomorrow evening.

4 a. I'll be on a date with Oscar.

   b. I'll be working late at the office.

5 a. I'll be sitting with my sister in the park.

   b. I'll be visiting my sister in New York.

6 a. I'll be visiting my uncle in the hospital.

   b. I'll be shipping a bundle to Boston.

7 a. How about sometime next spring?

   b. How about sometime in the spring?

8 a. I'll be seeing Harry next spring.

   b. I'll be getting married next spring.

HOW ABOUT YOU?

What will you be doing . . .

this evening? ....

tomorrow evening? ....

this weekend? ....

next Wednesday? ....

next spring? ....

WHAT DO YOU THINK?

What's your opinion of Gloria? What's your opinion of Arthur?

....

....

49.3 WHEN CAN YOU COME OVER? (55:11)

EDITING MIX-UP

The video editor made a mistake! Put the following lines in the correct order.

_____ I'm afraid I won't be home at five o'clock. I'll be playing baseball. How about six o'clock?

_____ I can come over at five o'clock. Is that okay?

__1__ I'm having some problems with the homework for tomorrow.

_____ Fine. I'll see you then.

_____ No, I won't be able to come over at six o'clock. I'll be having dinner. How about seven o'clock?

_____ I'll be glad to help. When can you come over?

WHAT DOES IT MEAN?

Choose the expression with the same meaning.

1 "I'm having some problems with the homework."

  a. There are a lot of problems on the homework.

  (b.) I'm having difficulty with the homework.

2 "I'll be glad to help."

  a. I can help you.

  b. I can't help you.

3 "I can come over at five o'clock. Is that okay?"

  a. I'll come over at five o'clock.

  b. Five o'clock is a good time for me.

4 "I'm afraid I won't be home at five o'clock."

  a. Come over then.

  b. Don't come over then.

5 "How about six o'clock?"

  a. Come over at six o'clock.

  b. Is six o'clock a good time for you?

6 "Fine. I'll see you then."

  a. That's a good time for me, too.

  b. I'm fine. How are you?

WRITE THE SCRIPT!

Complete this conversation and then practice it with a friend.

A. I'm having a problem with my car. Can you help me fix it?

B. Sure. ....

A. ....

B. ....

A. ....

B. Fine. I'll see you then.

49.4 WHAT DO YOU THINK? (55:40)

FINISH THE RAP!

call   do
hear   leave
phone   take
work

When do you think _____we'll be hearing_____ [1] from Anne?

I'm sure _____ [2] as soon as she can.

When do you think _____ [3] from Jack?

I'm sure _____ [4] as soon as he's back.

What do you think _____ [5] at two?

I think _____ [6] my kids to the zoo.

When do you think _____ [7] for Spain?

I think _____ [8] the four o'clock plane.

What do you think _____ [9] next spring?

I'm sure _____ [10] the same old thing.

What do you think _____ [11] next year?

As far as we know, _____ [12] right here.

On Side by Side TV!

RHYME TIME

Find the rhyming words in the rap.

1 Anne _____   4 Spain _____

2 Jack _____   5 spring _____

3 two _____   6 year _____

SORRY. I'LL BE _____ING!

The Side by Side TV cast members are trying to make plans, but they aren't having much success. Complete the following conversations any way you wish.

1. Oscar, can you help me practice my lines this afternoon?

Sorry. ....
....
....

2. Nancy, I'm having a party this Saturday evening. Can you come?

Sorry. ....
....
....

3. Jennifer and I are going out for dinner tomorrow. Do you want to join us, David?

Sorry. ....
....
....

4. Charles, do you want to go to the beach with me this Saturday? The weather is going to be beautiful!

Sorry. ....
....
....

5. Miyako, would you like to go to a movie with me on Friday?

Sorry. ....
....
....

6. Maria, I'm going to the gym to work out. Would you like to come with me?

Sorry. ....
....
....

7. We're all going to a restaurant after the show today. Can YOU come with us?

....
....
....

SEGMENT 49 SCRIPT ••••••••••••••••••••••••••••••••••

49.1 THE TELEPHONE COMPANY
(52:22)

SON: Hello.

FATHER: Hi, Bob. This is Dad.

SON: Oh hi, Dad. How are you?

FATHER: Pretty good.

SON: How's Mom?

FATHER: She's fine. So what's new with you?

SON: Nothing much. Everybody's okay here.

FATHER: That's good. I'm glad to hear that. Will you be home this evening?

SON: Yes, I will. I'll be reading.

FATHER: Oh. And how about Louise? Will she be home this evening?

SON: Yes, she will. She'll be writing some letters.

FATHER: What will Danny be doing?

SON: He'll be studying for a big math test.

FATHER: And how about Julie and Laura?

SON: They'll be playing with their toys and watching TV.

FATHER: Oh, that's nice. It sounds like you're all going to be very busy.

SON: Say, Dad, what will you and Mom be doing this evening?

FATHER: Oh, nothing much. I guess we'll be staying home.

SON: You'll be staying home?

FATHER: Yes. I suppose so.

SON: Well, I have a great idea.

FATHER: What's that, Bob?

SON: Can you and Mom come over for dinner this evening? We can have a nice dinner, and then you can play with the kids for a while.

FATHER: That sounds nice, Bob. Thank you.

SON: How's 6:30?

FATHER: 6:30? I'm sure that'll be fine. We'll see you then.

SON: Bye, Dad.

FATHER: Bye.

ANNOUNCER: Is there someone YOU should call? A message from your telephone company.

49.2 HI, GLORIA. THIS IS ARTHUR.
(54:08)

ARTHUR: Hi, Gloria. This is Arthur. Can I come over and visit this evening?

GLORIA: No, Arthur. I'm afraid I won't be home this evening. I'll be shopping at the supermarket.

ARTHUR: Oh. Can I come over and visit TOMORROW evening?

GLORIA: No, Arthur. I'm afraid I won't be home tomorrow evening. I'll be working late at the office.

ARTHUR: I see. Can I come over and visit this weekend?

GLORIA: No, Arthur. I'll be visiting my sister in New York.

ARTHUR: Oh. Well, can I come over and visit next Wednesday?

GLORIA: No, Arthur. I'll be visiting my uncle in the hospital.

ARTHUR: How about sometime next spring?

GLORIA: No, Arthur. I'll be getting married next spring.

ARTHUR: Oh!!

GLORIA: Good-bye.

BOYFRIEND: Good-bye, Arthur!

ARTHUR: Bye!

49.3 WHEN CAN YOU COME OVER?
(55:11)

FRIEND 1: I'm having some problems with the homework for tomorrow.

FRIEND 2: I'll be glad to help. When can you come over?

FRIEND 1: I can come over at five o'clock. Is that okay?

FRIEND 2: I'm afraid I won't be home at five o'clock. I'll be playing baseball. How about six o'clock?

FRIEND 1: No, I won't be able to come over at six o'clock. I'll be having dinner. How about seven o'clock?

FRIEND 2: Fine. I'll see you then.

49.4 WHAT DO YOU THINK? — GrammarRap (55:40)

When do you think we'll be hearing from Anne?
  I'm sure she'll be calling as soon as she can.
When do you think we'll be hearing from Jack?
  I'm sure he'll be phoning as soon as he's back.

What do you think you'll be doing at two?
  I think I'll be taking my kids to the zoo.
When do you think they'll be leaving for Spain?
  I think they'll be taking the four o'clock plane.

What do you think you'll be doing next spring?
  I'm sure I'll be doing the same old thing.
What do you think we'll be doing next year?
  As far as we know, we'll be working right here.
  On Side by Side TV!

GRAMMAR

Future Continuous Tense

(I will)	I'll	
(He will)	He'll	
(She will)	She'll	
(It will)	It'll	be working.
(We will)	We'll	
(You will)	You'll	
(They will)	They'll	

FUNCTION

Asking for and Reporting Information

Will you *be home this evening?*
  Yes, I will. I'll be *reading.*

I won't *be home this evening.*

Inquiring about Ability

When can you *come over?*

Expressing Ability

I can *come over at five o'clock.*

Offering a Suggestion

How about *six o'clock?*

Asking for Permission

Can I *come over and visit this evening?*

Expressing Agreement

Fine.
That'll be fine.

Greeting People

Hi, *Gloria.* This is *Arthur.*

Leave Taking

We'll see you then.

- **Future Continuous Tense**
- **Time Expressions**
- **Future Activities**

"How long will she be staying here? She'll be staying for a year . . . Side by Side."

LESSON MENU

SBS-TV Backstage Bulletin Board

TO: Production Crew
Sets and props for this segment:

Apartment	*Office*
couch	typewriter
violin	desk
suitcases	chair
telephone	report

TO: Cast Members
Key words in this segment:

for	violin
until	report
	public service announcement
return	
borrow	
disturb	
pilot	
medical school	
company	
take it easy	

50.1 BE NICE TO EVERYBODY (56:34)

SOUND CHECK

1
A. How much longer will you be practicing the violin?

B. I don't know. I guess

I'll be practicing

((for) until) another half hour.

2
A. How much longer will you be typing that report?

B. _____

it (for   until) five o'clock.

3
A. How long will your Aunt Gertrude be staying with us?

B. _____

with us (for   until) a few months.

LISTEN TO THE VOICE!

Listen and circle the words you hear.

VOICE: Now stop right (they're (there))¹!

GROUCHY GUY: Huh?

VOICE: Look at (yourselves yourself)².

You're (angry hungry)³.

(Your You're)⁴ upset.

And you're (hurting burning)⁵ lots of people.

GROUCHY GUY: I am?

VOICE: (Life Time)⁶ is short.

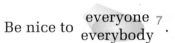

Be nice to (everyone everybody)⁷.

You'll be (happy happier)⁸.

GROUCHY GUY: Uh, well . . . okay.

VOICE: Let's start (right write)⁹ now.

GROUCHY GUY: Right (know now)¹⁰?

VOICE: Yes. Right now is a very good time.

PLEASANT GUY: Okay.

PLEASANT GUY: Aunt Gertrude, I'm so ~~glad~~ ~~mad~~ [11] you'll be staying with us for a few ~~months~~ ~~weeks~~ [12].

Here. ~~I'll take~~ ~~You can take~~ [13] those bags up to your room.

AUNT GERTRUDE: That's very ~~kind~~ ~~nice~~ [14] of you.

PLEASANT GUY: Brian? Nice job! This ~~report~~ ~~work~~ [15] is ~~excellent~~ ~~messy~~ [16]!

Thank you for all your hard work.

SECRETARY: ~~My pleasure~~ ~~I'm better~~ [17], sir.

PLEASANT GUY: William, that sounds ~~wonderful~~ ~~terrible~~ [18]!

You're playing so ~~beautifully~~ ~~softly~~ [19] these days.

SON: Gee! Thanks, Dad!

WHAT'S HE SAYING?

1. a.) Another half hour?! You've got to be kidding!

   b. William, that sounds wonderful!

2. a. Brian? Nice job! This report is excellent!

   b. Until five o'clock?! That's ridiculous!

3. a. I'm so glad you'll be staying with us for a few months.

   b. A few months?! I don't believe it!

50.2 WILL YOU BE HOME TODAY? (59:11)

EDITING MIX-UP

The video editor made a mistake! Put the following lines in the correct order.

_____ Oh. Then I won't come over at five.

_____ Yes, I will. I'll be cooking dinner.

_____ Okay. See you at five.

__1__ Hello, Richard. This is Julie. I want to return the tennis racket I borrowed from you last week. Will you be home today at about five o'clock?

_____ Why not?

_____ Don't worry. You won't disturb me.

_____ I don't want to disturb you. You'll be cooking dinner!

YES OR NO?

1	Richard is calling Julie.	Yes	(No)
2	He wants to return a tennis racket.	Yes	No
3	Julie borrowed the tennis racket last week.	Yes	No
4	Richard will be home today at about five o'clock.	Yes	No
5	He'll be studying English.	Yes	No
6	Julie says she won't come at five.	Yes	No
7	She wants to disturb him.	Yes	No
8	Julie will disturb Richard if she comes over at five.	Yes	No
9	Julie will be going over to Richard's house at five.	Yes	No

50.3 SBS-TV ON LOCATION (59:42)

WHAT ARE THEY SAYING?

What do you think you'll be doing ten years from now?

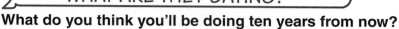

fly   live   take   go   run   work

_____I'll be flying_____[1] airplanes all over the world. I'm going to be a pilot!

_____[2] to medical school.

I guess _____[3]

in my father's store. And _____[4]

probably _____[5]
in my own apartment in the city.

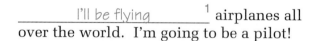

_____[6] my own company.

Hopefully, my wife and I

_____[7] in Florida.

And _____[8] it
easy for the first time in our lives!

THE NEXT LINE

Circle the best response.

1 How much longer will you be playing the piano?

   a. I like to play the piano.

   (b.) For about another fifteen minutes.

2 How much longer will you be doing your English homework?

   a. About eight o'clock.

   b. Until eight o'clock.

3 Let's start right now.

   a. Right now?

   b. Left now?

4 Let me help you wash the dishes.

   a. Will you be doing the dishes tomorrow?

   b. That's very kind of you.

5 You're playing the piano very well these days.

   a. Thanks!

   b. I'll play the piano every day.

6 What will you be doing in five years?

   a. I be living in Paris. (I hope!)

   b. I'll be living in Paris. (I hope!)

ANOTHER PUBLIC SERVICE ANNOUNCEMENT

Unscramble the sentences and discover a new Public Service Announcement from Side by Side TV!

1 Stop!   yourself!   at   Look

   Stop! Look at yourself.

2 selfish,   and tense.   You're   unkind,

3 think   yourself.   only   You   about

4 short.   is   Life   today.   someone   Help

5 happier,   too.   and   You'll   happier,   be   they'll   be

6 neighbor   right   Start   today.   and   now,   help   a

WEBSTER HIGH SCHOOL YEARBOOK

Look at this page from the Webster High School Yearbook. What do you think these students and Ms. Grant, the principal, will be doing ten years from now?

Michael Melanson
Math Club, Computer

Lisa Lane
French Club,
International Club

Mark Minton
Basketball,
Baseball, Hockey

Suzie and Barbie Burns
Theater Club

Miki Cheng
Basketball, Hockey,
Tennis

Jose Romero
Orchestra, Chorus

Ms. Grant
Principal

I think Michael will be studying mathematics at a university.

50.1 BE NICE TO EVERYBODY (56:34)

GROUCHY GUY: William?

SON: Yes, Dad?

GROUCHY GUY: How much longer will you be practicing the violin?

SON: I don't know. I guess I'll be practicing for another half hour.

GROUCHY GUY: Another half hour?! You've got to be kidding!

GROUCHY GUY: Brian?

SECRETARY: Yes, sir?

GROUCHY GUY: How much longer will you be typing that report?

SECRETARY: Well, uh . . . I'll be typing it until five o'clock, sir.

GROUCHY GUY: Until five o'clock?! That's ridiculous!

GROUCHY GUY: How long will your Aunt Gertrude be staying with us?

WIFE: She'll be staying with us for a few months.

GROUCHY GUY: A few months?! I don't believe it! A few months?!

VOICE: Now stop right there!

GROUCHY GUY: Huh?

VOICE: Look at yourself. You're angry. You're upset. And you're hurting lots of people.

GROUCHY GUY: I am?

VOICE: Life is short. Be nice to everybody. You'll be happier.

GROUCHY GUY: Uh, well . . . okay.

VOICE: Let's start right now.

GROUCHY GUY: Right now?

VOICE: Yes. Right now is a very good time.

PLEASANT GUY: Okay.

PLEASANT GUY: Aunt Gertrude, I'm so glad you'll be staying with us for a few months. Here. I'll take those bags up to your room.

AUNT GERTRUDE: That's very kind of you.

PLEASANT GUY: Brian? Nice job! This report is excellent! Thank you for all your hard work.

SECRETARY: My pleasure, sir.

PLEASANT GUY: William, that sounds wonderful! You're playing so beautifully these days.

SON: Gee! Thanks, Dad!

VOICE: Life is short. Be nice to everybody.

ANNOUNCER: A public service message from Side by Side TV.

50.2 WILL YOU BE HOME TODAY? (59:11)

JULIE: Hello, Richard. This is Julie. I want to return the tennis racket I borrowed from you last week. Will you be home today at about five o'clock?

RICHARD: Yes, I will. I'll be cooking dinner.

JULIE: Oh. Then I won't come over at five.

RICHARD: Why not?

JULIE: I don't want to disturb you. You'll be cooking dinner!

RICHARD: Don't worry. You won't disturb me.

JULIE: Okay. See you at five.

50.3 SBS-TV ON LOCATION (59:42)

INTERVIEWER: What do you think you'll be doing ten years from now?

PERSON 1: I'll be flying airplanes all over the world. I'm going to be a pilot!

PERSON 2: Ten years from now? I'll be going to medical school.

PERSON 3: Hmm. I guess I'll be working in my father's store. And I'll probably be living in my own apartment in the city.

PERSON 4: I'll be running my own company.

PERSON 5: Hopefully, my wife and I will be living in Florida.

PERSON 6: Or maybe Arizona.

PERSON 5: That's right. And we'll be taking it easy for the first time in our lives!

PERSON 6: We can't wait!

GRAMMAR

Future Continuous Tense

(I will)	I'll	
(He will)	He'll	
(She will)	She'll	
(It will)	It'll	be practicing.
(We will)	We'll	
(You will)	You'll	
(They will)	They'll	

Time Expressions

I'll be staying	for	another hour. a few months.
	until	five o'clock.

I'll be over	at five o'clock.
I'll be flying airplanes	in ten years.

FUNCTIONS

Inquiring about Intention

How much longer will you *be typing that report?*

Expressing Intention

I'll *be typing it until five o'clock.*

I won't *come over at five.*

Expressing Disapproval

Until five o'clock?! That's ridiculous!

You've got to be kidding!

Offering to Help

I'll *take those bags up to your room.*

Asking for and Reporting Information

How long will *your Aunt Gertrude be staying with us?*

Will you *be home today about five o'clock?*
Yes, I will. I'll *be cooking dinner.*

What do you think you'll *be doing ten years from now?*

Complimenting

Nice job! *This report is excellent!*

Expressing Gratitude

Thanks.

Thank you for *all your hard work.*

That's very kind of you.

Expressing Want-Desire

I want to *return the tennis racket I borrowed from you last week.*

Greeting People

Hello, *Richard.* This is *Julie.*

Leave Taking

See you *at five.*

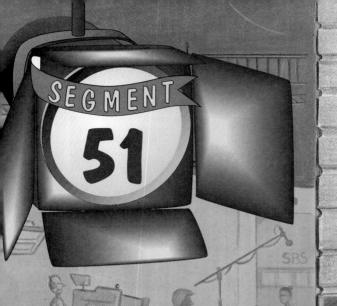

SEGMENT 51

- **Pronoun Review**
- **Verb Tense Review**

"It isn't mine or yours or his. I don't know whose watch this is . . . Side by Side."

SBS-TV Backstage Bulletin Board

TO: Production Crew
Sets and props for this segment:

Patio
bicycle
hose

Living Room
notebook
pencil
sofa
rocking chair
table
lamp

Locker Room
lockers
chairs
gym clothes
clock
bag
towels
sweatband
radio
weights
watch

TV Studio
chairs
script

TO: Cast Members
Key words in this segment:

get dressed
fix
complain
fall asleep
argue

tired
difficult
terrific

pleasure

watch
sweatband
locker room

I	he	she	you
me	him	her	you
my	his	her	your
myself	himself	herself	yourself

GRANDMOTHER: What's Johnny doing?

MOTHER: _____He_____'s¹ getting dressed.

GRANDMOTHER: Does _____² need any help? _____'ll³ be glad to help _____⁴.

MOTHER: No, that's okay. _____⁵ can get dressed by _____⁶.

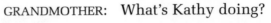

GRANDMOTHER: What's Kathy doing?

FATHER: _____'s⁷ fixing _____⁸ bicycle.

GRANDMOTHER: Does _____⁹ need any help. _____'ll¹⁰ be glad to help _____¹¹.

FATHER: No, that's okay, Mom. _____¹² can fix _____¹³ bicycle by _____¹⁴.

GRANDMOTHER: Oh, okay.

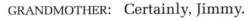

JIMMY: Grandma?

GRANDMOTHER: Yes, Jimmy?

JIMMY: _____¹⁵ need some help with _____¹⁶ math homework. Can _____¹⁷ help _____¹⁸?

GRANDMOTHER: Certainly, Jimmy.

JIMMY: Problem number four is very difficult. _____¹⁹ can't do it _____²⁰.

GRANDMOTHER: _____²¹ want _____²² to help _____²³? I'd be happy to. Let's take a look. Hmm. _____²⁴ know what, Jimmy? _____²⁵ can do problem number four by _____²⁶.

JIMMY: _____²⁷ can?

GRANDMOTHER: Yes, _____²⁸ can. Here. Look. First, you've got to do this. And then, _____²⁹ can do this.

JIMMY: Oh, now _____³⁰ get it, Grandma. Gee, _____'re³¹ terrific! Thanks.

GRANDMOTHER: It's _____³² pleasure, Jimmy.

Circle the word that tells what each sentence is expressing.

1 "Does he need any help?"	a. asking for help	(b.) offering help
2 "Can you help me?"	a. asking for help	b. offering help
3 "He can get dressed by himself."	a. ability	b. inability
4 "I need some help with my math homework."	a. asking for help	b. offering help
5 "I'll be glad to help him."	a. asking for help	b. offering help
6 "I can't do it myself."	a. ability	b. inability
7 "You can do problem number four by yourself."	a. ability	b. inability
8 "Oh, now I get it, Grandma."	a. understanding	b. inability
9 "Gee, you're terrific!"	a. complimenting	b. gratitude
10 "Thanks."	a. complimenting	b. gratitude

WHAT DO YOU THINK GRANDMA IS THINKING?

a. I'm so disappointed! Nobody needs me anymore!

b. Oh, well. Maybe I can help someone else.

c. Oh, good! They need my help!

a

1   2   3

FINISH THE SENTENCE!

d 1 Do you need ____?   a. help me

____ 2 I'll be glad ____.   b. by yourself

____ 3 Can you ____?   c. to help you

____ 4 You can do it ____.   d. any help

51.2 I JUST FOUND THIS (1:01:54)

EDITING MIX-UP

The video editor made a mistake! Put the following lines in the correct order.

1 ____ Okay. I will.

____ Really? I'll call him right away.

____ No, it isn't mine.

____ When you talk to him, tell him I said "Hello."

____ He lost his a few days ago.

__1__ I just found this watch. Is it yours?

____ But it might be Fred's.

2 ____ Oh, really? I'll call her when I get home. See you tomorrow.

____ No, it isn't mine.

____ Bye.

____ Maria? I just found this sweatband.

____ But, you know . . . I think it might be Jennifer's.

____ Is it yours?

____ She lost hers a few days ago.

YES OR NO?

1 Someone found a watch.   (Yes)   No

2 The watch could belong to Fred.   Yes   No

3 Fred lost his watch.   Yes   No

4 Gloria lost her sweatband.   Yes   No

5 Jennifer lost her sweatband.   Yes   No

6 Jennifer is going to call Gloria.   Yes   No

7 Maria and Gloria will see each other tomorrow.   Yes   No

••••• SEGMENT 51

WHOSE LINE?

1	"Hi, Michael."	Michael	(Miyako)
2	"You look tired today."	Michael	Miyako
3	"I couldn't fall asleep last night."	Michael	Miyako
4	"How late did they argue?"	Michael	Miyako
5	"That's terrible!"	Michael	Miyako
6	"I don't like to complain."	Michael	Miyako
7	"Well, I hope you sleep better tonight."	Michael	Miyako
8	"My neighbors don't argue very often."	Michael	Miyako
9	"MY neighbors sometimes argue early in the morning, . . ."	Michael	Miyako
10	"Poor guy!"	Michael	Miyako

YES OR NO?

1	Michael wasn't able to sleep last night.	(Yes)	No
2	He's exhausted today.	Yes	No
3	Michael's neighbors had a fight.	Yes	No
4	They were fighting until two A.M.	Yes	No
5	Michael asked his neighbors to make less noise.	Yes	No
6	Michael's neighbors argue very often.	Yes	No
7	Miyako's neighbors argue in the early morning.	Yes	No
8	Miyako falls asleep while she and Michael are talking.	Yes	No

HOW ABOUT YOU?

What are your neighbors like? Are you friendly with them? Do they ever argue?

....

....

RIGHT OR WRONG?

*If the sentence is correct, write **C**. If it is incorrect, write **I** and correct it.*

___I___ **1** I don't need any help. I can do it by me.

_____I can do it by myself._____

_____ **2** I found this ring on the floor. Is it your?

_____

_____ **3** Do you want me to help you?

_____

_____ **4** If you want some water, I help you.

_____

_____ **5** That bike isn't his. It belongs to hers.

_____

_____ **6** Is that him new car?

_____

_____ **7** I like they're new house very much.

_____

_____ **8** This doesn't belong to me. It's not me.

_____

WHICH WORD?

1 Miyako and Jennifer ⟨arrive / (arrived)⟩ late at the studio this morning.

2 Tim and Michael ⟨were going / will be going⟩ out for dinner tomorrow night.

3 The cast of Side by Side TV ⟨had / have⟩ a good time on the set last week.

4 Nancy and Oscar ⟨forgot / forget⟩ their lines this morning, but they say ⟨they remember / they'll remember⟩ them tomorrow.

5 At eight o'clock tomorrow morning, Alex and Tim ⟨will be driving / were driving⟩ to the studio.

6 After they ⟨finished / finish⟩ the SBS-TV video next week, Maria and Jennifer ⟨will be flying / flew⟩ to Los Angeles to make a TV commercial.

7 David ⟨is going / is going go to⟩ to Los Angeles, too. He's ⟨going to be / was⟩ in a movie.

8 Miyako and Jennifer ⟨like / like to⟩ work with each other. They always ⟨have / has⟩ fun together.

9 Gloria and Maria ⟨like / want⟩ to surprise Charles on his birthday today. They ⟨stayed up / will be staying up⟩ late last night and ⟨will bake / baked⟩ him a cake.

SEGMENT 51 SCRIPT ●●●●●●●●●●●●●●●●●●●●●●●●●●●●●●●●●●

51.1 I'LL BE GLAD TO HELP (1:00:28)

GRANDMOTHER: What's Johnny doing?
MOTHER: He's getting dressed.
GRANDMOTHER: Does he need any help? I'll be glad to help him.
MOTHER: No, that's okay. He can get dressed by himself.

GRANDMOTHER: What's Kathy doing?
FATHER: She's fixing her bicycle.
GRANDMOTHER: Does she need any help? I'll be glad to help her.
FATHER: No, that's okay, Mom. She can fix her bicycle by herself.
GRANDMOTHER: Oh, okay.

JIMMY: Grandma?
GRANDMOTHER: Yes, Jimmy?
JIMMY: I need some help with my math homework. Can you help me?
GRANDMOTHER: Certainly, Jimmy.
JIMMY: Problem number four is very difficult. I can't do it myself.
GRANDMOTHER: You want me to help you? I'd be happy to. Let's take a look. Hmm. You know what, Jimmy? You can do problem number four by yourself.
JIMMY: I can?
GRANDMOTHER: Yes, you can. Here. Look. First, you've got to do this. And then, you can do this.
JIMMY: Oh, now I get it, Grandma. Gee, you're terrific! Thanks.
GRANDMOTHER: It's my pleasure, Jimmy.

51.2 I JUST FOUND THIS (1:01:54)

FRIEND 1: I just found this watch. Is it yours?

FRIEND 2: No, it isn't mine. But it might be Fred's. He lost his a few days ago.
FRIEND 1: Really? I'll call him right away.
FRIEND 2: When you talk to him, tell him I said "Hello."
FRIEND 1: Okay. I will.

GLORIA: Maria? I just found this sweatband. Is it yours?
MARIA: No, it isn't mine. But, you know, I think it might be Jennifer's. She lost hers a few days ago.
GLORIA: Oh, really? I'll call her when I get home. See you tomorrow.
MARIA: Bye.

51.3 I COULDN'T FALL ASLEEP LAST NIGHT (1:02:38)

MIYAKO: Hi, Michael.
MICHAEL: Oh hi, Miyako.
MIYAKO: You look tired today.
MICHAEL: Yes, I know. I couldn't fall asleep last night.
MIYAKO: Why not?
MICHAEL: My neighbors were arguing.
MIYAKO: How late did they argue?
MICHAEL: Believe it or not, they argued until three A.M.!
MIYAKO: That's terrible! Did you call and complain?
MICHAEL: No, I didn't. I don't like to complain.
MIYAKO: Well, I hope you sleep better tonight.
MICHAEL: I'm sure I will. My neighbors don't argue very often.
MIYAKO: Well, you know . . . MY neighbors sometimes argue early in the morning, but they never argue late at night. Do your neighbors ever . . .

(Michael is asleep.)

Michael? Poor guy!

GRAMMAR

Pronoun Review

Subject Pronouns	Object Pronouns	Possessive Adjectives	Possessive Pronouns	Reflexive Pronouns
I	me	my	mine	myself
you	you	your	yours	yourself
he	him	his	his	himself
she	her	her	hers	herself
it	it	its	—	itself
we	us	our	ours	ourselves
you	you	your	yours	yourselves
they	them	their	theirs	themselves

FUNCTIONS

Asking for and Reporting Information

How *late did they argue?*

Offering to Help

I'll be glad to help you.

Do you need any help?

Asking for Help

I need some help *with my math homework.*

Expressing Ability

You can *do problem number four by yourself.*

Expressing Inability

I couldn't *fall asleep last night.*

I can't *do it myself.*

Inquiring about Ability

I can?

Declining an Offer

No, that's okay.

Expressing Possibility

It might be *Fred's.*

Expressing Intention

I'll *call her when I get home.*

Leave Taking

Bye.

See you tomorrow.

Expressing Hope

I hope *you sleep better tonight.*

Initiating a Topic

You look tired today.

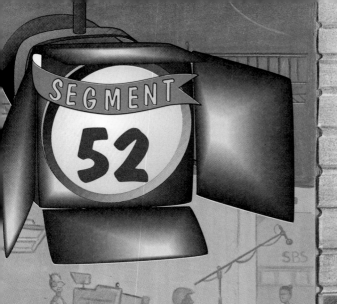

SEGMENT 52

- Some/Any
- Repair Problems
- Helping Friends

"Will anyone be home at ten? Somebody will be here then. . . . Side by Side."

LESSON MENU

SBS-TV Backstage Bulletin Board

TO: Production Crew
Sets and props for this segment:

Apartments
washing machine
kitchen sink
telephone

Plumbing Office
desk
chair
telephone

Side by Side Set
chair
letter
stool

TO: Cast Members
Key words in this segment:

somebody
anybody
something
anything

washing machine
kitchen sink

miss
remember
good-bye

mail

52.1 THERE'S SOMETHING WRONG WITH MY WASHING MACHINE (1:03:44)

YES OR NO?

1	The washing machine is working well.	Yes	(No)
2	There's something wrong with the washing machine.	Yes	No
3	Soap is coming out of the machine.	Yes	No
4	These people can fix the washing machine.	Yes	No
5	Somebody should look in the phone book to find the name of a repairperson.	Yes	No
6	They should hit and kick the washing machine. That will probably fix it.	Yes	No

SOUND CHECK

A. There's (something / anything)¹ wrong with my washing machine.

B. I'm sorry. I can't help you. I don't know something / anything ² about washing machines.

A. Do you know somebody / anybody ³ who can help me?

B. Not really. You should look in the phone book. I'm sure you'll find anybody / somebody ⁴ who can fix it.

HOW ABOUT YOU?

Can you fix things around the house? Tell about things you know how to fix, and tell how to fix them.

....

....

....

52.2 THERE'S SOMETHING WRONG WITH MY KITCHEN SINK

EDITING MIX-UP

(1:04:06)

The video editor made a mistake! Put the following lines in the correct order.

_____ Do you know anybody I can call?

_____ There isn't! You're right! Gee, Helen, I don't know anything about kitchen sinks.

_____ What's the matter with it?

_____ Thanks. I'll call them.

_____ Hmm. Yes. I know somebody. You should call the Armstrong Plumbing Company. They'll be able to fix it.

__1__ There's something wrong with my kitchen sink.

_____ Look! There isn't any water!

SOMETHING OR ANYTHING? SOMEONE OR ANYONE?

There's ___something___ [1] wrong with my printer. I don't know _____ [2] about printers, and I don't know _____ [3] who can fix it. So, I'll have to find _____ [4] to fix it for me.

There's _____ [5] wrong with my refrigerator. I don't know _____ [6] about refrigerators, and I don't know _____ [7] who knows about refrigerators. So, I guess I'll have to call _____ [8] to fix it for me.

SOUND CHECK

A. _____ Armstrong Plumbing Company _____ ¹. Can I help you?

B. Yes. There's _____ ² wrong with my kitchen _____ ³. Can you

send a _____ ⁴ to fix it as soon as possible?

A. Uh . . . Where do you live?

B. _____ ⁵ Grove Street in Centerville.

A. I can send a plumber tomorrow _____ ⁶. Is that okay?

B. Not really. I'm afraid _____ ⁷ home tomorrow morning.

_____ ⁸ my son to the dentist.

A. How about tomorrow afternoon?

B. _____ ⁹? What time?

A. Between _____ ¹⁰ and _____ ¹¹.

B. That's fine. _____ ¹² will be here then.

A. What's the name?

B. Helen Bradley.

A. And what's the address again?

B. _____ ¹³ Grove Street in Centerville.

A. And the phone number?

B. _____ ¹⁴.

A. Okay. We'll have someone there tomorrow _____ ¹⁵.

B. Thank you.

52.4 IT'S TIME TO SAY GOOD-BYE (1:05:19)

All of the Side by Side TV cast members are very sorry it's the end of the program. Watch the scene, and put a check only next to the lines you hear.

_____ **1** "I'm really sorry Side by Side TV is over."

✔ **2** "I can't believe it's over."

_____ **3** "Too bad. It was great to work with all of you."

_____ **4** "It's a shame it had to end."

_____ **5** "I'm going to miss you all. I feel like we were a family."

_____ **6** "I wish it wasn't ending."

_____ **7** "I'm going to really miss all of you."

_____ **8** "I really regret it's over."

_____ **9** "We're going to miss you, too."

_____ **10** "I'm sorry it's over."

WHAT'S NEXT?

_b_ **1** Remember the day I moved to my new apartment? I didn't have enough money to pay a moving company, and I couldn't move everything myself, . . .

_____ **2** I remember the week my refrigerator was broken.

_____ **3** Remember when Jennifer had the hiccups?

_____ **4** And I remember the day you all surprised me with a birthday cake!

a. That was fun.

b. . . . so all of you came over and helped. I'll never forget that.

c. I remember that. And David helped me.

d. You all brought me dinner . . . every day! It was wonderful!

CLOSE-UP

Tell about something special you remember about Side by Side TV.

....

....

SCRIPT CHECK 1

Write all the expressions of "good-bye" you hear.

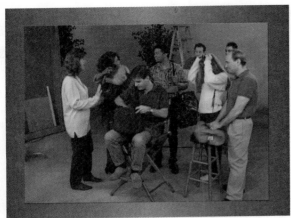

1 *Bye.* _____

2 _____

3 _____

4 _____

5 _____

6 _____

7 _____

8 _____

SCRIPT CHECK 2

Watch the scene again and check the number of times you hear the following:

Bye	Good-bye

Total _____   _____

FIND THE RHYMING WORDS!

Read and listen to the letter from the President of the Side by Side TV Network, and complete the rhyming words.

Dear Side by Side TV Cast Members:

Thank you all so very much.

We really liked your __show__¹.

We're sure you're feeling very sad

That now it's time to _____².

Our audience really loves you.

They're calling and asking for _____³.

So please come back tomorrow

For Side by Side Levels Three and _____⁴!

WRAP-UP

MATCH!

Choose the correct words to say "good-bye."

_c_ **1** I guess it's time _____.

_____ **2** Take care of _____.

_____ **3** See you _____.

_____ **4** So _____.

_____ **5** Take _____.

_____ **6** I'm going to _____.

a. miss you all

b. long

c. to say "good-bye"

d. soon

e. yourself

f. it easy

CLOSE-UP

You're on Side by Side TV! Tell the words you use to say "good-bye" in your country. What gestures do you use? Do you hug like the Side by Side TV cast members? Do you kiss, bow, or shake hands?

....

....

....

....

....

52.1 THERE'S SOMETHING WRONG WITH MY WASHING MACHINE (1:03:44)

FRIEND 1: There's something wrong with my washing machine.

FRIEND 2: I'm sorry. I can't help you. I don't know anything about washing machines.

FRIEND 1: Do you know anybody who can help me?

FRIEND 2: Not really. You should look in the phone book. I'm sure you'll find somebody who can fix it.

52.2 THERE'S SOMETHING WRONG WITH MY KITCHEN SINK (1:04:06)

HELEN BRADLEY: There's something wrong with my kitchen sink.

FRIEND: What's the matter with it?

HELEN BRADLEY: Look! There isn't any water!

FRIEND: There isn't! You're right! Gee, Helen, I don't know anything about kitchen sinks.

HELEN BRADLEY: Do you know anybody I can call?

FRIEND: Hmm. Yes. I know somebody. You should call the Armstrong Plumbing Company. They'll be able to fix it.

HELEN BRADLEY: Thanks. I'll call them.

52.3 CAN YOU SEND A PLUMBER? (1:04:35)

PLUMBER: Armstrong Plumbing Company. Can I help you?

HELEN BRADLEY: Yes. There's something wrong with my kitchen sink. Can you send a plumber to fix it as soon as possible?

PLUMBER: Uh . . . Where do you live?

HELEN BRADLEY: 156 Grove Street in Centerville.

PLUMBER: I can send a plumber tomorrow morning. Is that okay?

HELEN BRADLEY: Not really. I'm afraid I won't be home tomorrow morning. I'll be taking my son to the dentist.

PLUMBER: How about tomorrow afternoon?

HELEN BRADLEY: Tomorrow afternoon? What time?

PLUMBER: Between one and four.

HELEN BRADLEY: That's fine. Somebody will be here then.

PLUMBER: What's the name?

HELEN BRADLEY: Helen Bradley.

PLUMBER: And what's the address again?

HELEN BRADLEY: 156 Grove Street in Centerville.

PLUMBER: And the phone number?

HELEN BRADLEY: 237-9180.

PLUMBER: Okay. We'll have someone there tomorrow afternoon.

HELEN BRADLEY: Thank you.

52.4 IT'S TIME TO SAY *GOOD-BYE*
(1:05:19)

ALEX: Well, guys, I can't believe it's over.

DAVID: No more Side by Side TV.

GLORIA: Yeah. Too bad. It was great to work with all of you.

MICHAEL: We had a lot of fun.

MARIA: I'm going to miss you all. I feel like we were a family.

NANCY: We WERE a family, Maria, and we still ARE.

CHARLES: You're right, Nancy. And I'm going to really miss all of you.

JENNIFER: Oh, Charles, we're going to miss you, too.

OSCAR: Remember the day I moved to my new apartment? I didn't have enough money to pay a moving company, and I couldn't move everything myself, so all of you came over and helped. I'll never forget that.

MIYAKO: That's what friends are for, Oscar.

GLORIA: I remember the week my refrigerator was broken. You all brought me dinner . . . every day! It was wonderful!

TIM: Remember when Jennifer had the hiccups?

JENNIFER: I remember that. And David helped me.

MIYAKO: And I remember the day you all surprised me with a birthday cake!

MICHAEL: That was fun.

ALEX: Well, I guess it's time to say "good-bye."

DAVID: Bye.

NANCY: Good-bye.

OSCAR: Take care of yourself.

MICHAEL: See you soon.

MARIA: Take care.

CHARLES: Take it easy.

TIM: See ya.

MIYAKO: Good-bye.

JENNIFER: Bye.

GLORIA: So long.

ALEX: Bye.

(The cast leaves. A studio assistant arrives with a letter.)

STUDIO
ASSISTANT: Hey, uh . . . hey, wait a minute! I have mail for Side by Side TV cast members. Anybody? Side by Side TV cast . . . mail call! Tim?

(Tim opens the letter.)

TIM: Hey, you guys, come back! It's from the President of the Side by Side TV Network.

CAST: Wow! Oh!

TIM: "Dear Side by Side TV Cast Members,
Thank you all so very much.
We really liked your show.
We're sure you're feeling very sad
That now it's time to go.
Our audience really loves you.
They're calling and asking for more.
So please come back tomorrow
For Side by Side Levels Three and Four!"

(The cast cheers.)

GRAMMAR

Some/Any

> There's **something** wrong with my washing machine.
> I'm sure you'll find **somebody/someone** who can fix it.
>
> I don't know **anything** about washing machines.
> Do you know **anybody/anyone** who can help me?

FUNCTIONS

Asking for and Reporting Information

There's something wrong with *my washing machine.*

Do you know *anybody who can help me?*

I won't *be home tomorrow morning.*
I'll be *taking my son to the dentist.*

What's the name?
  Helen Bradley.
And what's the address again?
  156 Grove Street in Centerville.
And the phone number?
  237-9180.

Expressing Inability

I can't *help you.*

Offering Advice

You should *look in the phone book.*

Identifying

Armstrong Plumbing Company.

Offering to Help

Can I help you?

Inquiring about Agreement

Is that okay?

Expressing Agreement

That's fine.

Expressing Regret

I can't believe it's over.

It's too bad.

I'm going to miss *you all.*

Remembering

Remember *when Jennifer
  had the hiccups?*

I remember *that.*

Leave Taking

Bye.
Good-bye.

Take care of yourself.
Take care.
Take it easy.

See you.
See you soon.
So long.

ANSWER KEY ●●●●●●●●●●●●●●●●●●●●●●●●●●●●●●●●

SEGMENT 40

PAGE 2

DIRECTION CHECK
1. D
2. D

EDITING MIX-UP
 4
 2
 5
 1
 3

PAGE 3

FINISH THE SCRIPT!
1. Take
2. get off
3. Second
4. Walk up
5. on the right
6. Take
7. get off
8. Walk down
9. on the left
10. Take
11. get off
12. Walk up
13. on the left

PAGE 4

YES OR NO?
1. Yes
2. No
3. Yes
4. Yes
5. No
6. Yes

PAGE 5

SOUND CHECK
1. Take the subway
2. get off
3. Seventh
4. Walk down
5. Seventh
6. on your right

FUNCTION CHECK
1. a
2. a
3. b
4. a
5. b
6. b
7. a

DID YOU NOTICE?
1. c
2. a
3. e
4. d
5. b

PAGE 6

GETTING AROUND SUNNYVILLE
1. Take
2. get off
3. Walk up
4. on the left/ on your left
5. Take
6. get off
7. Walk down
8. on the right/ on your right
9. Take
10. get off
11. First Street
12. Walk up First Street and you'll see the park on the left/on your left.

SEGMENT 41

PAGE 10

YES OR NO?
1. No
2. Yes
3. No
4. Yes
5. No
6. No
7. Yes
8. No

WHAT'S THE LINE?
1. a
2. b
3. a
4. b
5. b
6. a

PAGE 11

SOUND CHECK
1. beautiful, beautifully
2. good, well
3. magnificent, magnificently
4. graceful, gracefully
5. fast, fast
6. accurate, accurately
7. slow, slowly

PAGE 12

THE NEXT LINE
1. a
2. b
3. b
4. a
5. a
6. b

SCRAMBLED SOUND TRACK
HUSBAND: Well, I think that's enough TV for tonight.
WIFE: Good night, dear. Sleep well!

PAGE 13

OPPOSITES
1. d
2. a
3. b
4. f
5. c
6. e

SOUND CHECK
1. quickly, slowly
2. softly, louder
3. sloppily, neatly
4. late, earlier
5. impolitely, politely
6. carelessly, carefully

PAGE 14

YES OR NO?
1. Yes
2. No
3. No
4. Yes
5. No
6. No
7. No
8. Yes
9. Yes
10. No
11. No
12. No
13. Yes

MATCH THE PHRASES!
1. c
2. a
3. d
4. b

PAGE 15

SOUND CHECK
1. careful
2. carefully
3. careful
4. carefully
5. beautiful
6. beautifully
7. beautiful
8. beautifully
9. graceful
10. gracefully
11. graceful
12. gracefully
13. stronger
14. longer
15. better
16. better

PAGE 16

THE PEOPLE IN GARY'S OFFICE
1. Karen speaks to her co-workers unprofessionally. She should speak to them more professionally.
2. Mike answers the telephone impolitely. He should answer it more politely.
3. Ray writes reports incorrectly. He should write them more correctly.
4. The bookkeeper keeps the books inaccurately. She should keep them more accurately.
5. Amy makes presentations ineffectively. She should make them more effectively.
6. The president runs the company inefficiently. He should run it more efficiently.

PAGE 17

A LETTER TO A FRIEND
1. exciting
2. well
3. better
4. slowly
5. excellent
6. inexpensive
7. cheaply
8. nutritiously
9. friendly
10. quickly
11. nicer
12. polite
13. pleasant
14. carefully
15. courteously
16. pleased

SEGMENT 42

PAGE 22

YES OR NO?
1. No
2. No
3. No
4. Yes
5. Yes
6. No
7. Yes
8. No
9. Yes
10. No
11. No

SOUND CHECK
1. I feel, I'll come
2. don't, I'll probably go
3. I can't, I'll call

PAGE 23

WHAT ARE THEY SAYING?
1. b
2. a
3. a
4. b
5. a
6. b
7. b
8. a
9. b
10. b

SOUND CHECK
1. they have, they'll name
2. they have, they'll name

GIFT IDEAS
1. it's, she'll give
2. it's, she'll give

PAGE 24

SOUND CHECK
1. is
2. I'll work
3. is
4. I'll
5. it's
6. I'll
7. it rains
8. I'll
9. I have
10. I'll stay
11. I don't
12. I'll

PAGE 25

SOUND CHECK
1. shouldn't drive
2. drive
3. might have
4. shouldn't eat
5. eat
6. might get
7. shouldn't talk
8. talk
9. might hit
10. shouldn't play
11. play
12. might hurt
13. park
14. might get
15. might stay

PAGE 26

SHERMAN'S MOODS
1. pleasant
2. pleasant
3. annoyed
4. annoyed
5. angry
6. angry
7. sad

PAGE 28

SCRAMBLED SOUND TRACK
1. If you find a four-leaf clover, you'll have good luck.
2. If you open an umbrella in your house, you'll have bad luck.
3. If you break a mirror, you'll have bad luck for seven years.
4. If your right ear itches, somebody is saying good things about you.
5. If your left ear itches, somebody is saying bad things about you.
6. If you find a horseshoe, you'll have good luck.

PAGE 29

EDITING MIX-UP
  3
  1
  5
  6
  4
  8
  9
  7
  2

PAGE 30

TOO MUCH ADVICE!
1. shouldn't
2. stay
3. might be
4. shouldn't
5. play
6. might be
7. shouldn't
8. forget
9. shouldn't
10. forget
11. might
12. shouldn't
13. talk
14. might
15. shouldn't
16. you're
17. might
18. shouldn't
19. read
20. might be
21. you're
22. might
23. shouldn't
24. throw
25. might

SEGMENT 43

PAGE 36

SOUND CHECK
1. were
2. doing
3. was washing
4. was giving
5. was washing
6. were watching
7. were doing

PAGE 37

EDITING MIX-UP
  7
  4
  1
  5
  2
  6
  3
  8

PAGE 38

YES OR NO?
1. Yes
2. No
3. Yes
4. No
5. Yes
6. Yes

WHAT WAS EVERYBODY DOING?
1. b
2. a
3. b
4. a

PAGE 39

WHAT'S HAPPENING?
1. b
2. a
3. b
4. a
5. a
6. b

PAGE 40

WHAT'S HAPPENING?
1. a
2. b
3. b
4. b
5. a
6. b
7. a
8. b
9. b
10. a

MATCH!
1. d
2. c
3. e
4. a
5. b

PAGE 41

SOUND CHECK
1. were
2. doing
3. was washing
4. was visiting
5. were having
6. was playing
7. were attending
8. was visiting

PAGES 42–43

WRITE THE SCRIPT!
1. were entering
2. were
3. doing
4. was carrying
5. was watching
6. were looking
7. was standing
8. was looking
9. was wearing
10. was wearing
11. was holding
12. were playing
13. was pushing
14. was jogging
15. was delivering
16. was listening
17. was planting
18. were sitting
19. were watching
20. drove away
21. honked
22. did
23. have
24. had

PAGE 44

DO YOU REMEMBER?
1.	b	9.	a
2.	a	10.	b
3.	a	11.	b
4.	b	12.	b
5.	a	13.	a
6.	b	14.	b
7.	b	15.	b
8.	b		

WHAT WERE THEY DOING?
Possible answers are:
1. What were they playing?
2. What were they washing?
3. What were they listening to?
4. What were they having/eating?
5. What were they watching?
6. What were they paying?

SEGMENT 44
PAGE 50

SCENE CHECK
1.	b	7.	b
2.	b	8.	b
3.	a	9.	b
4.	b	10.	a
5.	a	11.	a
6.	b	12.	b

PAGE 51

SCENE CHECK
1.	b	5.	b
2.	b	6.	a
3.	a	7.	b
4.	a	8.	b

SCRIPT CHECK
itself	*ourselves*
1	2
yourselves	*themselves*
1	2

PAGE 52

EDITING MIX-UP
1.
    3
    5
    4
    1
    2

2.
    2
    1
    4
    3
    5

PAGE 53

SOUND CHECK
1. burned myself while dinner
2. hurt myself while bowling
3. poked himself eye Ouch!
4. cut herself while slicing

THE NEXT LINE
1.	b	5.	b
2.	b	6.	b
3.	b	7.	a
4.	b	8.	a

PAGE 54

ON CAMERA
1.	No	5.	Yes
2.	Yes	6.	Yes
3.	No	7.	Yes
4.	Yes	8.	No

PAGE 55

FINISH THE LINES!
1. look themselves
2. talks herself
3. get dressed himself
4. clean ourselves
5. study myself
6. turns itself
7. teach herself
8. enjoy yourselves

SEGMENT 45
PAGE 60

SOUND CHECK
1.	Could	9.	homework
2.	play	10.	couldn't
3.	basketball	11.	tired
4.	little	12.	Could
5.	couldn't	13.	eat
6.	short	14.	wedding
7.	Could	15.	couldn't
8.	finish	16.	nervous

PAGE 61

SCENE CHECK
1.	a	7.	b
2.	a	8.	b
3.	a	9.	a
4.	b	10.	b
5.	a	11.	b
6.	a	12.	a

PAGE 62

EDITING MIX-UP
1.
    2
    1
    4
    3

2.
    4
    5
    1
    3
    2
    6

3.
    4
    2
    6
    1
    5
    3

THE NEXT LINE
1.	b	5.	b
2.	a	6.	a
3.	b	7.	b
4.	a	8.	a

PAGE 63

COMPLETE THE CONVERSATION
1. *Never Say Couldn't*
2. shy
3. couldn't talk
4. couldn't go
5. couldn't speak
6. nervous
7. couldn't fly
8. couldn't drive
9. couldn't
10. take
11. Never say couldn't
12. couldn't
13. scared
14. nervous
15. Never say couldn't

PAGE 65

SOUND CHECK
1.	Was	7.	wasn't able to
2.	able to	8.	spicy
3.	wasn't able to	9.	Were
4.	heavy	10.	able to
5.	Was	11.	weren't able to
6.	able to	12.	difficult

YES OR NO?
1. No
2. No
3. Yes
4. Yes
5. Yes
6. No
7. No

WHAT'S THE WORD?

1. wasn't
2. was
3. weren't
4. were
5. weren't, was

PAGE 66

SOUND CHECK

1. enjoy
2. wasn't able to
3. had to
4. enjoy
5. couldn't
6. had to

WHAT HAPPENED?

1. b
2. a
3. b
4. b
5. b
6. a

PAGE 67

DO YOU REMEMBER?

1. a
2. b
3. b
4. b
5. b

PAGE 68

MATCH!

1. e
2. d
3. i
4. l
5. b
6. j
7. a
8. g
9. k
10. f
11. h
12. c

THE RIGHT WORD

1. weren't
2. could
3. had to
4. was able
5. weren't
6. couldn't
7. had
8. couldn't
9. had to

SEGMENT 46

PAGE 74

YES OR NO?

1. Yes
2. Yes
3. No
4. No
5. Yes
6. Yes
7. Yes
8. No
9. Yes
10. No
11. Yes
12. No
13. Yes
14. Yes
15. No
16. Yes
17. No
18. No
19. No

PAGE 75

EDITING MIX-UP

4
3
7
5
2
6
1

THE NEXT LINE

1. a
2. b
3. a
4. b
5. a
6. b

WHO IS EVERYBODY?

1. c
2. f
3. b
4. d
5. a
6. e

PAGE 76

WHOSE LINE?

1. C
2. A
3. B
4. B
5. D
6. A
7. C
8. D
9. B

FUNCTION CHECK

1. a
2. a
3. b
4. b
5. b
6. a
7. a
8. b
9. a
10. b

PAGE 77

WHAT DOES IT MEAN?

1. b
2. b
3. b
4. a
5. b
6. a
7. b
8. b

DID YOU NOTICE?

1. Yes
2. No
3. No
4. Yes
5. No
6. No
7. Yes
8. No

PAGE 78

EDITING MIX-UP

3
2
1
4

MORE EXCUSES

1. won't be able to, I've got to, I'll be able to
2. won't be able to, I've got to, I'll be able to
3. won't be able to, We've got to
4. won't be able to, She's got to, she'll be able to
5. won't be able to, He's got to, he'll be able to
6. won't be able to, We've got to

PAGE 79

YES OR NO?

1. Yes
2. Yes
3. No
4. Yes
5. No
6. No
7. Yes
8. No
9. Yes
10. Yes
11. Yes

EDITING MIX-UP

3
1
4
2
7
6
9
5
8

PAGE 80

FINISH THE SONG!

1. day
2. today
3. go
4. no
5. to
6. do
7. play
8. day
9. day
10. today
11. go
12. no
13. to
14. do

PAGE 81

EVEN MORE EXCUSES!

1. won't be able to
2. it's got to
3. he'll be able to
4. won't be able to
5. she's got to
6. she'll be able to
7. won't be able to
8. he'll be able to
9. will be able to
10. will be able to

WHAT DO YOU SAY?

1. b
2. a
3. a
4. a

SEGMENT 47
PAGE 86

MORE, LESS, OR FEWER?

	more	less	fewer
1.		✔	
2.			✔
3.	✔		
4.		✔	
5.	✔		
6.			✔
7.		✔	
8.	✔		
9.			✔

SCENE CHECK

1. b
2. a
3. b
4. b
5. b
6. b
7. a
8. b
9. b
10. a
11. a

PAGE 87

PREDICTING

1. less
2. fewer
3. more
4. fewer, less
5. more
6. less
7. Less, more

SOUND CHECK

1. diets
2. fewer
3. these
4. less
5. this
6. more
7. that
8. too much
9. exercise
10. exercise

PAGE 88

SCENE CHECK

1. must
2. don't have to
3. mustn't

THEY WENT TO THE DOCTOR TODAY

1. must
2. mustn't
3. don't have to, mustn't
4. mustn't
5. must, don't have to, must
6. must, don't have to, must

PAGE 89

EDITING MIX-UP

```
  2
  1
  8
  3
  5
  6
  4
  7
```

PAGE 90

THE RIGHT WORD

1. more
2. a few
3. less
4. more
5. mustn't
6. shouldn't
7. have to
   don't have to
8. Should

MY DENTIST SAYS . . .

1. d
2. a
3. c
4. e
5. b

SEGMENT 48
PAGE 94

WHAT'S HAPPENING?

1. a
2. b
3. b
4. b

OTHER PEOPLE'S PROBLEMS

1. musn't
2. must
3. mustn't
4. mustn't

PAGE 95

YES OR NO?

1. No
2. No
3. Yes
4. No
5. Yes
6. No
7. Yes
8. No
9. No

WHAT DOES IT MEAN?

1. b
2. b
3. b
4. a
5. b

PAGE 96

SCRAMBLED SOUND TRACK

1. You should stay in bed and rest.
2. You should drink lots of fluids: water, juice, whatever. That'll help.
3. You should take a nice hot shower and breathe in the hot, steamy air. You'll feel a lot better.
4. When I have a cold, I drink hot tea with lemon.
5. Chicken soup. It's the best medicine for a cold. Believe me. I know what I'm talking about. Have some chicken soup, and your cold will disappear, just like that!

PAGES 97–98

SCENE CHECK

1. b
2. b
3. b
4. a
5. b
6. b
7. b
8. a
9. b
10. b
11. b
12. b
13. b
14. a
15. a
16. b
17. a
18. b
19. b
20. a

PAGE 98

MORE ADVICE

1. c
2. d
3. b
4. a

PAGE 99

EDITING MIX-UP

```
1.  8
    5
    1
    6
    2
    7
    4
    3

2.  3
    4
    2
    1

3.  3
    1
    4
    2
    5
```

FINISH THE SENTENCE!

1. d
2. j
3. g
4. i
5. h
6. a
7. e
8. b
9. f
10. c

PAGE 101

THE BEST RESPONSE

1. c
2. f
3. e
4. b
5. a
6. g
7. d

MUST OR SHOULD?

1. S
2. M
3. M
4. S
5. S
6. M
7. S
8. S
9. S
10. S

SEGMENT 49

PAGE 106

EDITING MIX-UP 1

3
1
5
7
4
2
6

WHAT WILL EVERYBODY BE DOING?

1. I'll be reading
2. She'll be writing
3. will
4. be doing
5. He'll be studying
6. They'll be playing
7. watching
8. will
9. be doing
10. we'll be staying
11. You'll be staying

PAGE 107

EDITING MIX-UP 2

7
5
2
4
8
3
1
6

THE RIGHT RESPONSE

1. b
2. e
3. d
4. a
5. f
6. c

PAGE 108

LINE CHECK

1. b
2. b
3. a
4. b
5. b
6. a
7. a
8. b

PAGE 109

EDITING MIX-UP

4
3
1
6
5
2

WHAT DOES IT MEAN?

1. b
2. a
3. b
4. b
5. b
6. a

PAGE 110

FINISH THE RAP!

1. we'll be hearing
2. she'll be calling
3. we'll be hearing
4. he'll be phoning
5. you'll be doing
6. I'll be taking
7. they'll be leaving
8. they'll be taking
9. you'll be doing
10. I'll be doing
11. we'll be doing
12. we'll be working

RHYME TIME

1. can
2. back
3. zoo
4. plane
5. thing
6. here

SEGMENT 50

PAGE 116

SOUND CHECK

1. I'll be practicing   for
2. I'll be typing   until
3. She'll be staying   for

LISTEN TO THE VOICE!

1. there
2. yourself
3. angry
4. You're
5. hurting
6. Life
7. everybody
8. happier
9. right
10. now
11. glad
12. months
13. I'll take
14. kind
15. report
16. excellent
17. My pleasure
18. wonderful
19. beautifully

PAGE 117

WHAT'S HE SAYING?

1. a   2. b   3. a

PAGE 118

EDITING MIX-UP

3
2
7
1
4
6
5

YES OR NO?

1. No
2. No
3. Yes
4. Yes
5. No
6. Yes
7. No
8. No
9. Yes

PAGE 119

WHAT ARE THEY SAYING?

1. I'll be flying
2. I'll be going
3. I'll be working
4. I'll
5. be living
6. I'll be running
7. will be living
8. we'll be taking

PAGE 120

THE NEXT LINE

1. b
2. b
3. a
4. b
5. a
6. b

ANOTHER PUBLIC SERVICE ANNOUNCEMENT

1. Stop! Look at yourself!
2. You're unkind, selfish, and tense. *or* You're selfish, unkind, and tense.
3. You only think about yourself.
4. Life is short. Help someone today.
5. You'll be happier, and they'll be happier, too.
6. Start right now, and help a neighbor today.

SEGMENT 51

PAGE 126

SOUND CHECK

1. He
2. he
3. I
4. him
5. He
6. himself
7. She
8. her
9. she
10. I
11. her
12. She
13. her
14. herself
15. I
16. my
17. you
18. me
19. I
20. myself
21. You
22. me
23. you
24. You
25. You
26. yourself
27. I
28. you
29. you
30. I
31. you
32. my

PAGE 127

FUNCTION CHECK
1. b
2. a
3. a
4. a
5. b
6. b
7. a
8. a
9. a
10. b

WHAT DO YOU THINK GRANDMA IS THINKING?
1. c
2. a
3. b

FINISH THE SENTENCE!
1. d
2. c
3. a
4. b

PAGE 128

EDITING MIX-UP
1.
7
5
2
6
4
1
3

2.
6
3
7
1
4
2
5

YES OR NO?
1. Yes
2. Yes
3. Yes
4. No
5. Yes
6. No
7. Yes

PAGE 129

WHOSE LINE?
1. Miyako
2. Miyako
3. Michael
4. Miyako
5. Miyako
6. Michael
7. Miyako
8. Michael
9. Miyako
10. Miyako

YES OR NO?
1. Yes
2. Yes
3. Yes
4. No
5. No
6. No
7. Yes
8. No

PAGE 130

RIGHT OR WRONG?
1. I   I can do it by myself.
2. I   Is it yours?
3. C
4. I   If you want some water, I'll help you.
5. I   It belongs to her.
6. I   Is that his new car?
7. I   I like their new house very much.
8. I   It's not mine.

WHICH WORD?
1. arrived
2. will be going
3. had
4. forgot, they'll remember
5. will be driving
6. finish, we'll be flying
7. is going, going to be
8. like to, have
9. want, stayed up, baked

SEGMENT 52

PAGE 134

YES OR NO?
1. No
2. Yes
3. Yes
4. No
5. Yes
6. No

SOUND CHECK
1. something
2. anything
3. anybody
4. somebody

PAGE 135

EDITING MIX-UP
5
4
2
7
6
1
3

SOMETHING OR ANYTHING? SOMEONE OR ANYONE?
1. something
2. anything
3. anyone
4. someone
5. something
6. anything
7. anyone
8. someone

PAGE 136

SOUND CHECK
1. Armstrong Plumbing Company
2. something
3. sink
4. plumber
5. 156
6. morning
7. I won't be
8. I'll be taking
9. Tomorrow afternoon
10. one
11. four
12. Somebody
13. 156
14. 237-9180
15. afternoon

PAGE 137

WHAT ARE THEY SAYING?
_____ 1.
✔ 2.
✔ 3.
_____ 4.
✔ 5.
_____ 6.
✔ 7.
_____ 8.
✔ 9.
_____ 10.

WHAT'S NEXT?
1. b
2. d
3. c
4. a

PAGE 138

SCRIPT CHECK 1
1. Bye.
2. Good-bye.
3. Take care of yourself.
4. See you soon.
5. Take care.
6. Take it easy.
7. See ya.
8. So long.

SCRIPT CHECK 2
Bye   *Good-bye*
3   3

FIND THE RHYMING WORDS!
1. show
2. go
3. more
4. Four

PAGE 139

MATCH!
1. c
2. e
3. d
4. b
5. f
6. a